Sd. Kfz. 161

Pz. IV Ausf. G/H/J

vol. 2

Waldemar Trojca

Katowice – Speyer 2005

MODEL HOBBY
ul. Opolska 2, 40-084 Katowice, POLAND
tel./fax: (0-32) 258 89 33
www.modelhobby.pl
e-mail: modelhobby@modelhobby.pl

© Trojca

Series design & layout: Waldemar Trojca
Cover designed by: Waldemar Trojca
Color plates designed by: Waldemar Trojca
Color plates and cover artwork by: Waldemar Trojca i „F14"
Scanning and digital work:
Waldemar Trojca, Andrzej Szewczyk
Translated by: John Fedorowicz
Proofreading: muse M, John Fedorowicz
Printed in Poland by: Małopolska Poligrafia Sp.j., 30-390 Kraków,
ul. Zawiła 69, tel.: (0-12) 262 03 06

ISBN: 83-60041-02-4

From the Autor Warning!

I wish to inform any readers of the published volumes 6 and 7 (and the announced volume 8) from the Pz.Kpfw. V Panther series of books by AJ-Press that I did not have the opportunity to edit them and that they are based on materials prepared by myself several years ago. I can not accept any responsibility for any errors which occur in them, as well as any photographs from Hideya Ando that have been placed in them. The drawings signed by S. Zajączkowski have been *pirated* and most of them do not compare in quality to my drawings used in the series. This fact I will not comment on further.

Other titels available:

In preparation:

Exclusive distributor of the English edition of the Book for the following regions and/or countries:
a) North America, b) South America, c) Hong Kong, d) Japan and Singapore
J.J. Fedorowicz Publishing, Inc.
104 Browning Boulevard, Winnipeg, Manitoba, Canada R3K 0L7
Tel: (204) 837-6080, Fax:(204)889-1960
e-mail: jjfpub@jjfpub.mb.ca web: www.jjfpub.mb.ca

© Copyright Waldemar Trojca:

Klappe

Motorklappe

Lüfterklappe

Kühlerklappe

Panzerkastenoberteil

Klappe

Klappe

Kommandantenkuppel

Zwölfuhrzeigertrieb

MP.-Klappe

Drehbühne

Turmzurrung

Turm

Federausgleicher

Zwölfuhrzeiger

Walzenblende

Höhenrichtmaschine

7,5 cm Kw.K. 40

Kugelblende 50

Fahreroptik

Fahrersehklappe 50

Pz.Kpfw.IV Ausf.G

3

Kühlluftaustritt

8/7,5 cm Patronen

21 Gurtsäcke mit insgesamt 3150 Patronen MG - Munition

Turmzielfernrohr 5d

Turmstirnwand

Sehklappe

Zielschiene

24/7,5 cm Patronen

4/7,5 cm Patronen

4/7,5 cm Patronen

18/7,5 cm Patronen

6/7,5 cm Patronen

23/7,5 cm Patronen

Pz.Kpfw.IV Ausf.G

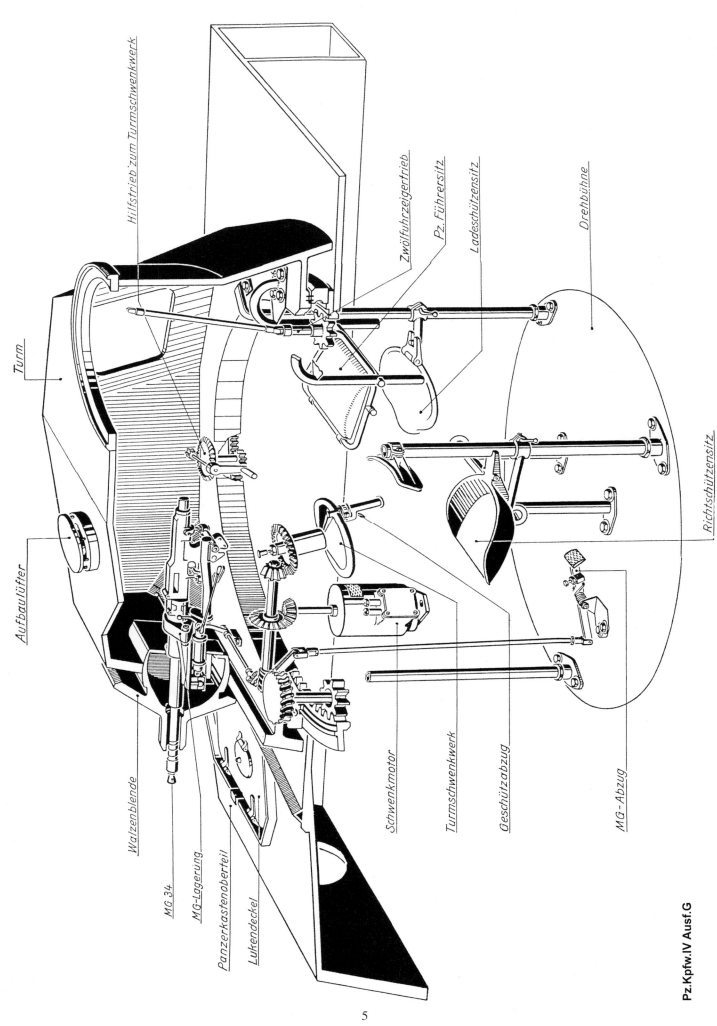

Hilfstrieb zum Turmschwenkwerk

Zwölfuhrzeigertrieb

Pz. Führersitz

Ladeschützensitz

Drehbühne

Turm

Aufbaulüfter

Richtschützensitz

Walzenblende

MG 34

MG-Lagerung

Panzerkastenoberteil

Lukendeckel

Schwenkmotor

Turmschwenkwerk

Geschützabzug

MG - Abzug

Pz.Kpfw.IV Ausf.G

Pz.Kpfw.IV Ausf.H (7.PD), Rozhishche, Eastern Front, 02.44. This early production series tank carries a Filzbalg-Vorschaltluftfilter air filter mounted on the mud guard.

Pz.Kpfw.IV Ausf.G, Inside of the turret, showing the commander's and loader's stations.

Pz.Kpfw.IV Ausf.G, Eastern Front, 02.43

Pz.Kpfw.IV Ausf.G, (SS-Panzer-Regiment 1 *Leibstandarte SS Adolf Hitler*?), Charkov, 03.43. During long road marches, very often two 200 liter barrels were carried next to the turret as extra fuel containers. Obviously, this manner of transporting extra fuel was only possible in areas reasonably far behind the combat zone.

Pz.Kpfw.IV Ausf.G, Eastern Front, 1943. This tank must have been acting as an ambulance as, on a handle of the rear hull wall, it carries a container with the red cross.

Pz.Kpfw.IV Ausf.G, Eastern Front, 1943

Pz.Kpfw.IV Ausf.G
(05.1943)

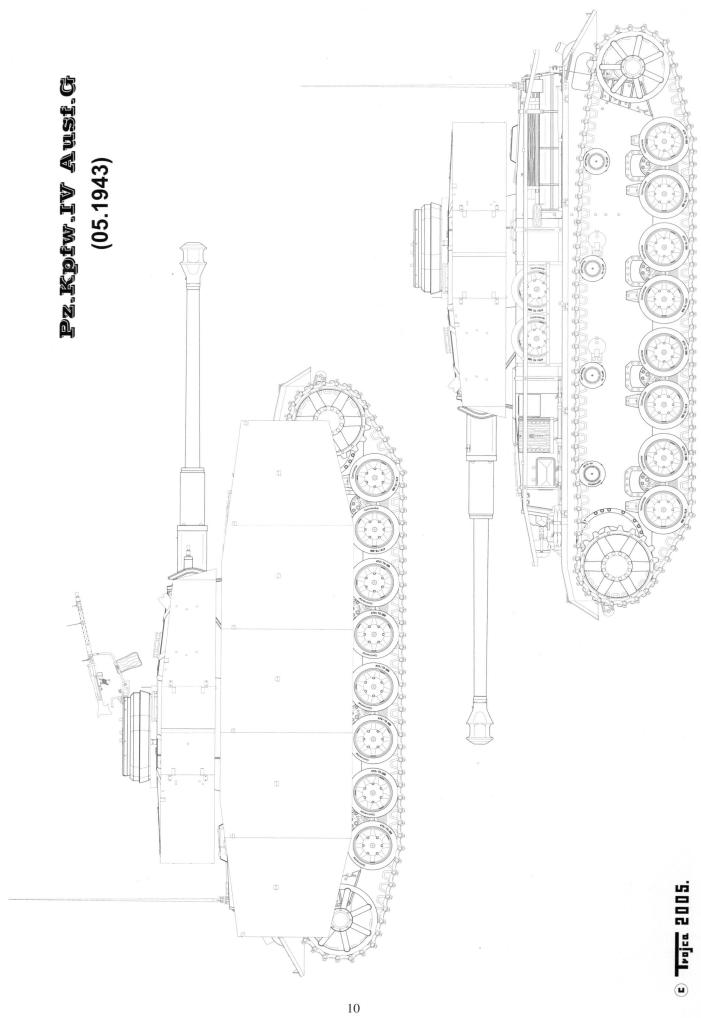

Pz.Kpfw.IV Ausf.G
(05.1943)

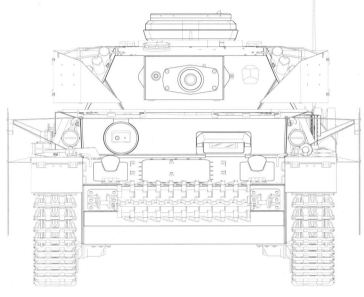

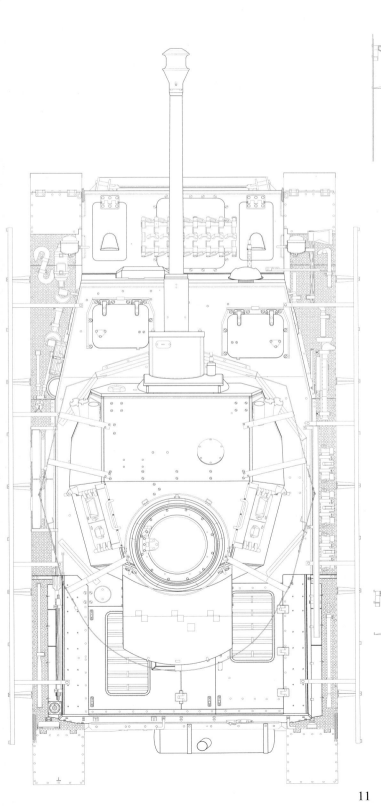

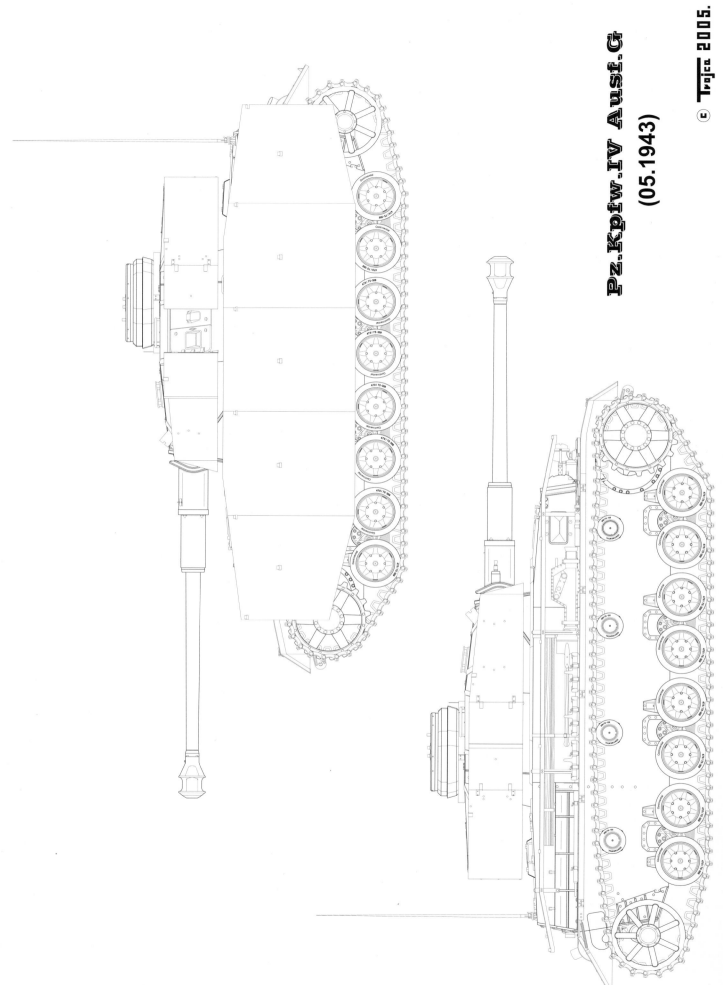

Pz.Kpfw.IV Ausf.G
(05.1943)

© Trojca 2005.

12

Pz.Kpfw.IV Ausf.H (Sd.Kfz.161/1)

The production of the **Pz.Kpfw.IV Ausf.H** variant began in the first days of 05.43 and ended in 02.44. Altogether, 2,322 of this variant were built; 379 by Krupp, 693 by Vomag and 1,250 by Nibelungenwerk. Construction-wise, the **Pz.Kpfw.IV Ausf.H** was practically identical to the final production series of the **Pz.Kpfw.IV Ausf.G**. Among the most significant changes on the **Ausf.H** was the increase in the thickness of the front glacis and superstructure armor to 80 mm (initially, it was 50 mm, with a bolted-on 30 mm armor plate) and the increase in the thickness of the roof armor (the front part to 16 mm and the rear part to 25 mm). During the production of the tank, many other smaller improvements and changes were carried out. Those were, mainly, to simplify and speed up the production process. In the workshops of the combat units, very often during overhauls of the **Ausf.H** variant parts from the **Ausf.G** were used (and vice versa). This makes it difficult to positively identify many photos which are currently considered to represent tanks of the **Ausf.G** or **Ausf.H** variants.

Among the more important changes made during production were; starting in 09.43, the elimination of the observation slits on the sides of the superstructure, a change in the mountings for the Schurzen side skirts (brought in during 10.43), starting in 12.43, the use of a toothed joint in the linking of the front and side armor plates of the superstructure (this was not done in all the produced **Ausf.H's**), and the addition of the Nahverteidigungswaffe, which, as on the Panther, was supposed to have been mounted on the tanks already by the end of 1943. However, the opening in the roof meant for that weapon was covered with a plate (screwed on) on most of the tanks. A few of the tanks had the launcher installed, but starting only in 06.44. The engine filter (Filzbalgvorschaltluftfilter) with the armor cover, which was installed from 05.43, did not perform adequately as it had a tendency to dirty very quickly and become plugged. As a result, its mounting in the tank ended in 02.44.

The main armament of the **Pz.Kpfw.IV Ausf.H** was the 75 mm KwK.40 (L/48) gun. Its ammunition load was 87 rounds, and the MG ammunition load was 3,150 rounds. The combat weight of the tank was 25,000 kilograms (That of the **Ausf.G** was 23,600 kg).

The technical data for the **Pz.Kpfw.IV Ausf.H** is as follows:

Total length	7,020 mm
Maximum width	2,880 mm
Height with turret	2,680 mm
Ground clearance	400 mm
Track width	400 mm
Distance between centers of tracks	2,456 mm
Maximum speed	
a) highway	38 km/h (cruising 25 km/h)
b) cross-country	20 km/h
Range	
a) highway	210 km
b) cross-country	130 km

Pz.Kpfw.IV Ausf.J (Sd.Kfz.161/2)

The production of the **Pz.Kpfw.IV Ausf.J** variant began in the first days of 02.44 and ended in 04.45. A total of 3,150 tanks of this variant were built; 180 by Vomag and 2,970 by Nibelungenwerk. Construction-wise, the **Pz.Kpfw.IV Ausf.J** was almost identical to the **Pz.Kpfw.IV Ausf.H**. However, a fundamental change was the elimination of the electric mechanism for rotating the turret. After the powering unit (DKW) was removed, in the rear of the hull was placed an additional 210 liter fuel tank (total fuel capacity was 680 liters). That fuel tank caused problems as it was not sealed properly. As a result of the threat of fire, the fuel tank was not installed in the tanks for a period of time. During the production of the tank, many other improvements and changes were carried out. They were, mainly, to simplify and speed up the production process. Among some of the more important were; simplification of the design of the road wheels (with one ring seal), the use of steel return rollers, and the reduction of the number of return rollers from 4 to 3 per side (from 08.06.44). From 09.44, the Flammentöter flame suppressors were installed on the exhaust pipes. The design of the escape hatches for the driver and radio operator was simplified, and the observation slits and MP-Klappe (for firing small arms) on the turret side hatches were eliminated. However, though this change was already made in 05.44, these turret hatches were still used until the end of the series production. As on other tanks, from 14.06.44, three eyelets were installed on the turret roof for mounting the small portable crane, which had a lifting capacity of up to 2,000 kilograms. These eyelets were also installed on the **Ausf.G** and **Ausf.H** variants already in service.

The main armament of the **Pz.Kpfw.IV Ausf.J** was the 75 mm KwK.40 (L/48) gun. Its ammunition load was 87 rounds, and the MG ammunition load was 3,150 rounds. The combat weight of the tank was 25,000 kilograms.

The technical data for the **Pz.Kpfw.IV Ausf.J** is as follows:

Total length	7,020 mm
Maximum width	2,880 mm
Height with turret	2,680 mm
Ground clearance	400 mm
Track width	400 mm
Distance between centers of tracks	2,456 mm
Maximum speed	
a) highway	38 km/h (cruising 25 km/h)
b) cross-country	20 km/h
Range	
a) highway	320 km
b) cross-country	210 km

All variants of the **Pz.Kpfw.IV** were powered by the Maybach HL 120 TRM engine (based on the Maybach HL 100, with increased capacity), which was produced by the firm of Maybach Motorenbau in Friedrichschafen.

Technical data of engine:

Number of cylinders	12
Angle between banks	60 degrees
Engine type	four-stroke
Stroke	115 mm
Bore	105 mm
Capacity	11,867 cc
Compression ratio	6.8:1
Engine output (at 2,600 revs/min)	265 hp
Maximum output (at 3,000 revs/min)	300 hp
Neutral gear revolutions	800 revs/min
Carburetors	2 x Soles 40 JFF 2
Starter	1 BNG 4/24 electric starter
Generator	2 x GTLN 600/12/1500/LS/26
Firing order of cylinders	1-12-5-8-3-10-6-7-2-11-4-9
Weight of engine (including starter, oil cooler and generator, but without oil or coolant/water)	ca 920 kilograms,

Pz.Kpfw.IV Ausf.H (16.Pz.Div.) An early production series tank with the additional, 30 mm thick, bolted-on armor plate.

Sd.Kfz.161/2 – Pz.Kpfw.IV Ausf.H

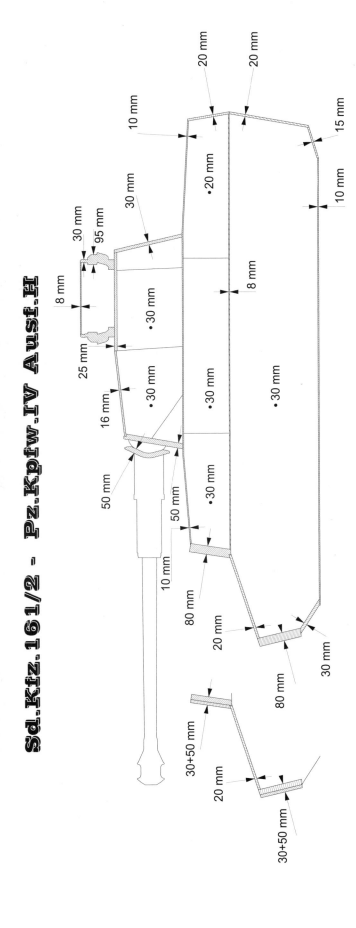

Sd.Kfz.161/2 – Pz.Kpfw.IV Ausf.J

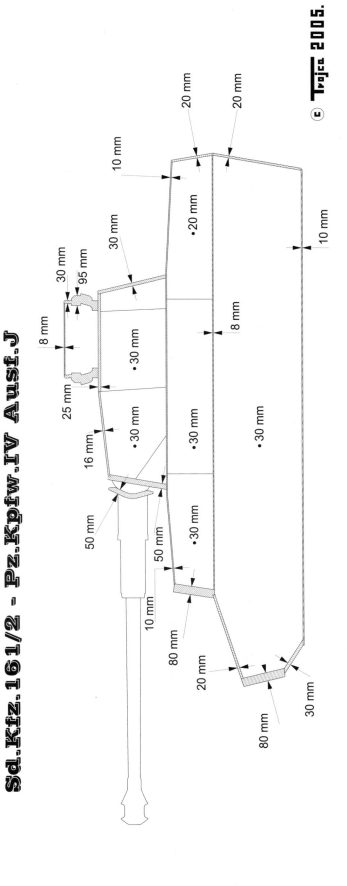

Pz.Kpfw.IV Ausf.H, Eastern Front, 1943. This early production series tank has added bolted-on armor plate (30 mm thick).

Pz.Kpfw.IV Ausf.H (16.Pz.Div.) An early production series tank with the additional, 30 mm thick, bolted-on armor plate.

Pz.Kpfw.IV Ausf.H (6./SS-Pz.Rgt.1 *Leibstandarte SS Adolf Hitler*), Mailand, 11.08.43
An early production series tank with the additional, 30 mm thick, bolted-on armor plate.

Pz.Kpfw.IV Ausf.H (Unterscharführer Gerhard Arnold, 6./SS-Pz.Rgt.1 *Leibstandarte SS Adolf Hitler*), Mailand, 11.08.43

18

Pz.Kpfw.IV Ausf.H, An early production series tank with the additional, 30 mm thick, bolted-on armor plate.

Pz.Kpfw.IV Ausf.H, An early production series tank with the additional, 30 mm thick, bolted-on armor plate.

Pz.Kpfw.IV Ausf.H, Eastern Front, 1944. This tank has been photographed while evacuating wounded soldiers. It has spare track links, as additional protection for the crew, mounted on the front and side of the hull, and on the front and roof of the turret.

Pz.Kpfw.IV Ausf.H, Eastern Front, 1944

Pz.Kpfw.IV Ausf.H, France, 1944

Pz.Kpfw.IV Ausf.H, Italy, 10.43

Pz.Kpfw.IV Ausf.H (26.Pz.Div.), Italy, 09.43

Pz.Kpfw.IV Ausf.H, Italy, 1943. The destroyed tank in this photograph carries the Filzbalg-Vorschaltluftfilter air filter mounted on the mud guard.

Pz.Kpfw.IV Ausf.H, Italy, 04.45

Pz.Kpfw.IV Ausf.H, Salerno, 23.08.43

Pz.Kpfw.IV Ausf.H, Eastern Front, 1943

Pz.Kpfw.IV Ausf.H, Eastern Front, Orel, 08.44

Pz.Kpfw.IV Ausf.H (16.Pz.Div.), Eastern Front, 03.1944

Pz.Kpfw.IV Ausf.H, (II./Pz.Rgt.GD), Eastern Front, 02.1944

Pz.Kpfw.IV Ausf.J, Eastern Front, 1944

Pz.Kpfw.IV Ausf.H, France, 08.44

Pz.Kpfw.IV Ausf.H (Unterscharführer Willy Kretzschmar, 5./II.Abt.SS-Pz.Rgt.12 of the 12.SS-Pz.Div.*Hitlerjugend*), Normandy, 06.44

Pz.Kpfw.IV Ausf.H (6./II.Abt.SS-Pz.Rgt.12 of the 12.SS-Pz.Div.*Hitlerjugend*), Normandy, 06.44

Pz.Kpfw.IV Ausf.H (6./II.Abt.SS-Pz.Rgt.12 of the 12.SS-Pz.Div.*Hitlerjugend*), Belgium, 1944

Pz.Kpfw.IV Ausf.H (5./II.Abt.SS-Pz.Rgt.12 of the 12.SS-Pz.Div.*Hitlerjugend*), Normandy, 06.44. In the Normandy fighting, due to the complete Allied air superiority, the camouflaging of armored vehicles was an absolute necessity for the Germans.

Pz.Kpfw.IV Ausf.H (Oberscharführer Terdenge, 6./II.Abt.SS-Pz.Rgt.12 of the 12.SS-Pz.Div.*Hitlerjugend*), France, 1944

Pz.Kpfw.IV Ausf.H (6./Pz.Rgt.35 of the 4.Pz.Div.), Eastern Front, 1944

Pz.Kpfw.IV Ausf.H (546, 7.PD), Eastern Front, Lutsk, 01.44

Pz.Kpfw.IV Ausf.H (546, 7.PD), Eastern Front, 03.44

Pz.Kpfw.IV Ausf.H (7.PD), Eastern Front, 1944

Pz.Kpfw.IV Ausf.H

Pz.Kpfw.IV Ausf.H, Eastern Front, 1944

Pz.Kpfw.IV Ausf.H (546, 7.PD), Eastern Front, Schepetowka, 01.44. The tank shown in this series of photos (it cannot be ruled out that this is a later version of an **Ausf.G**) displays the usual combat wear and tear, such as some missing mud guards. It also carries spare track links on the front and side of the hull and the front of the turret, which were placed there as additional protection for the crew (and the next 3 pages).

Pz.Kpfw.IV Ausf.J, Eastern Front, 1944, Trank links from a Soviet T-34 were used as extra protection on this tank.

Pz.Kpfw.IV Ausf.H, Normandy, 06.44

Pz.Kpfw.IV Ausf.J, France, 1944

Pz.Kpfw.IV Ausf.J, Eastern Front, 1945

Pz.Kpfw.IV Ausf.J, Luxemburg, 12.44

Pz.Kpfw.IV Ausf.J (Kampfgruppe Peiper, SS-Pz.Rgt. 1), Bastogne, 26.12.44

Pz.Kpfw.IV Ausf.J, Hungaria, 1945

Pz.Kpfw.IV Ausf.J, Hungaria, 1945

Pz.Kpfw.IV Ausf.J (**Pz.Bef.Wg.IV?**) This tank from the final production series carries the Drahtgeflechtschürzen wire mesh side skirts..

Pz.Kpfw.IV Ausf.H
(06.1943)

46

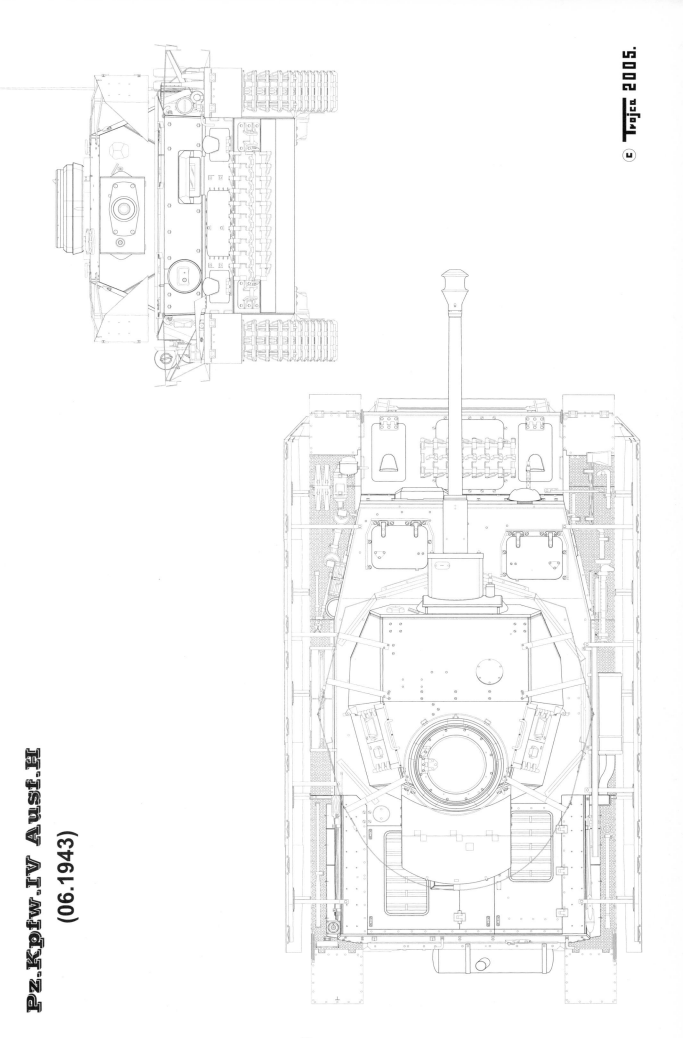

Pz.Kpfw.IV Ausf.H
(06.1943)

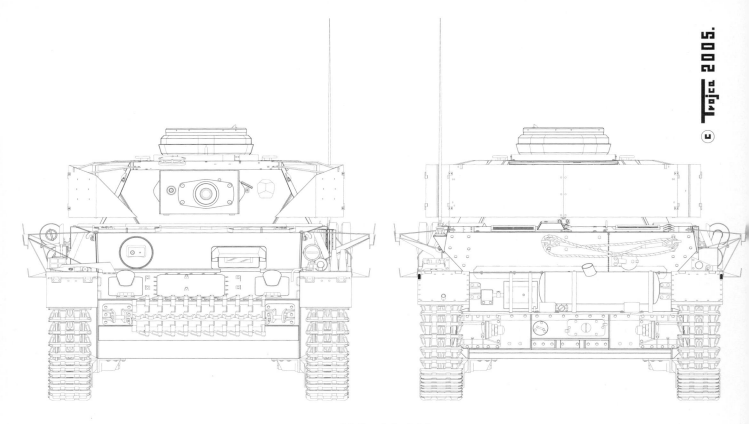

(08.1943)

Pz.Kpfw.IV Ausf.H

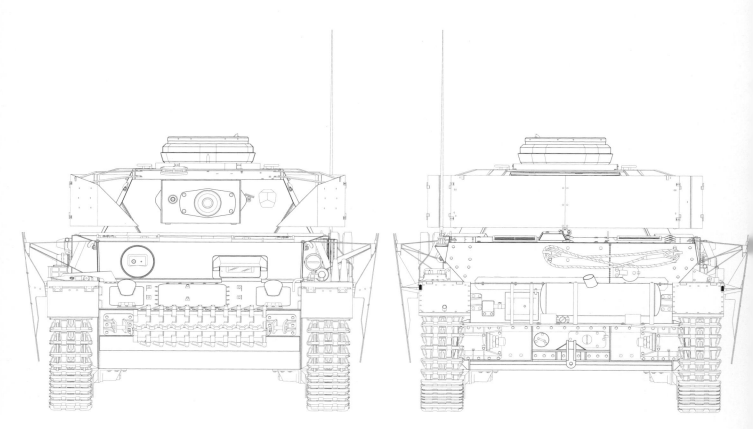

(02.1944)

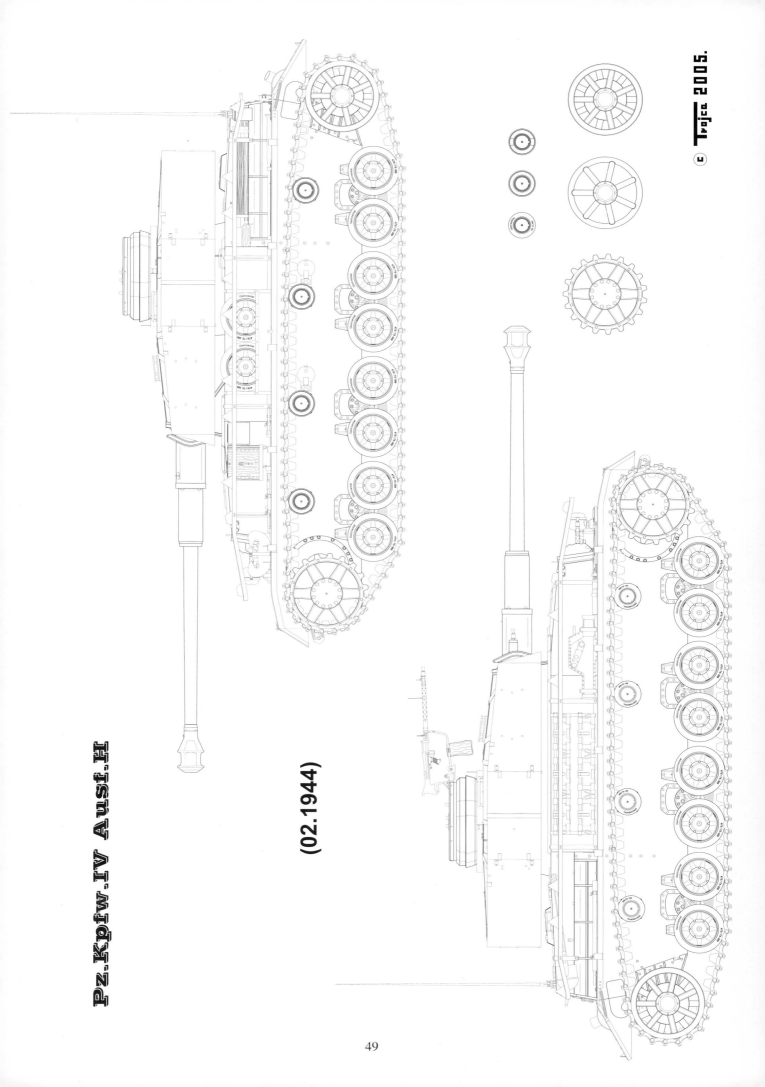

Pz.Kpfw.IV Ausf.H

(02.1944)

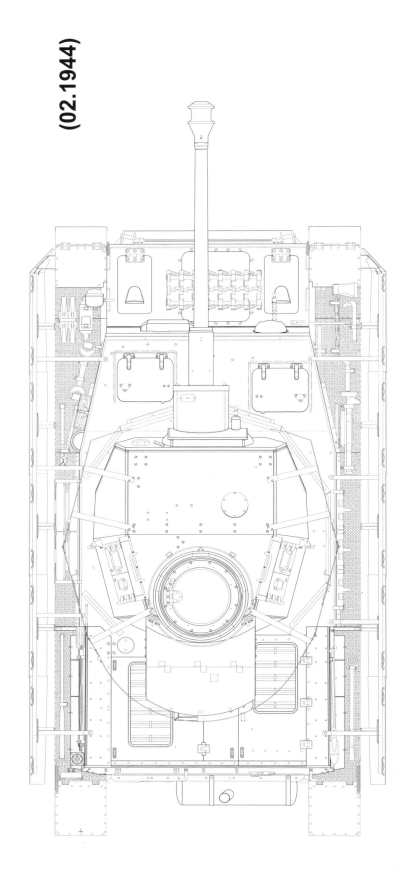

© Trojca 2005.

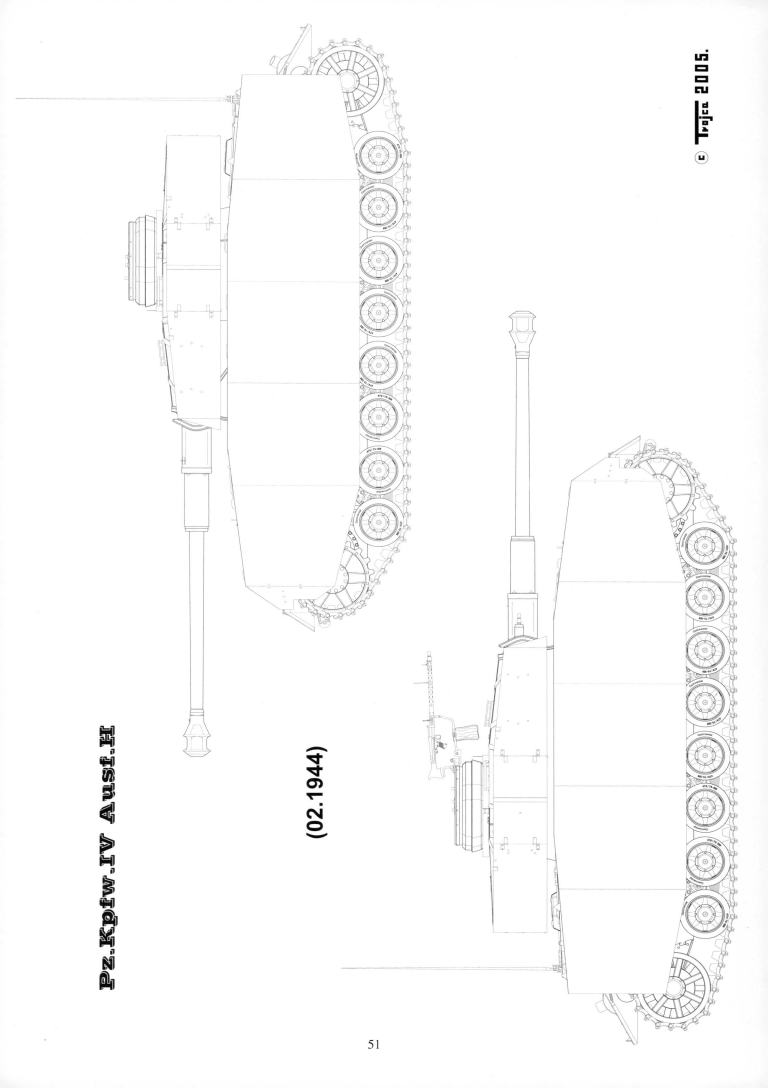

Pz.Kpfw.IV Ausf.H

(02.1944)

(05.1944)

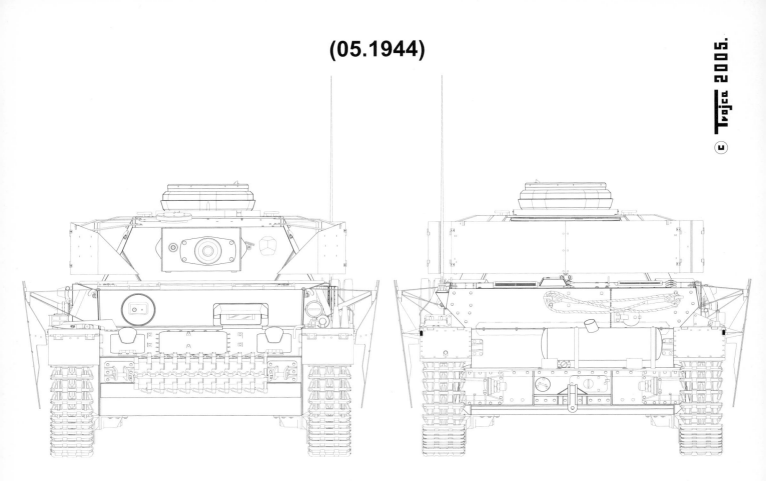

Pz.Kpfw.IV Ausf.J

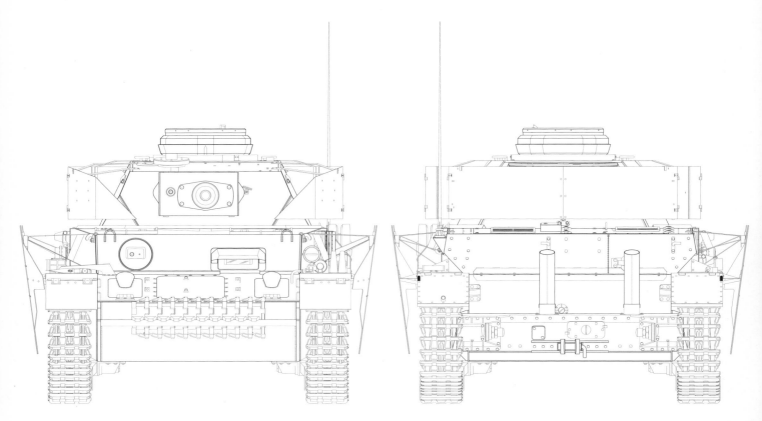

(04.1945)

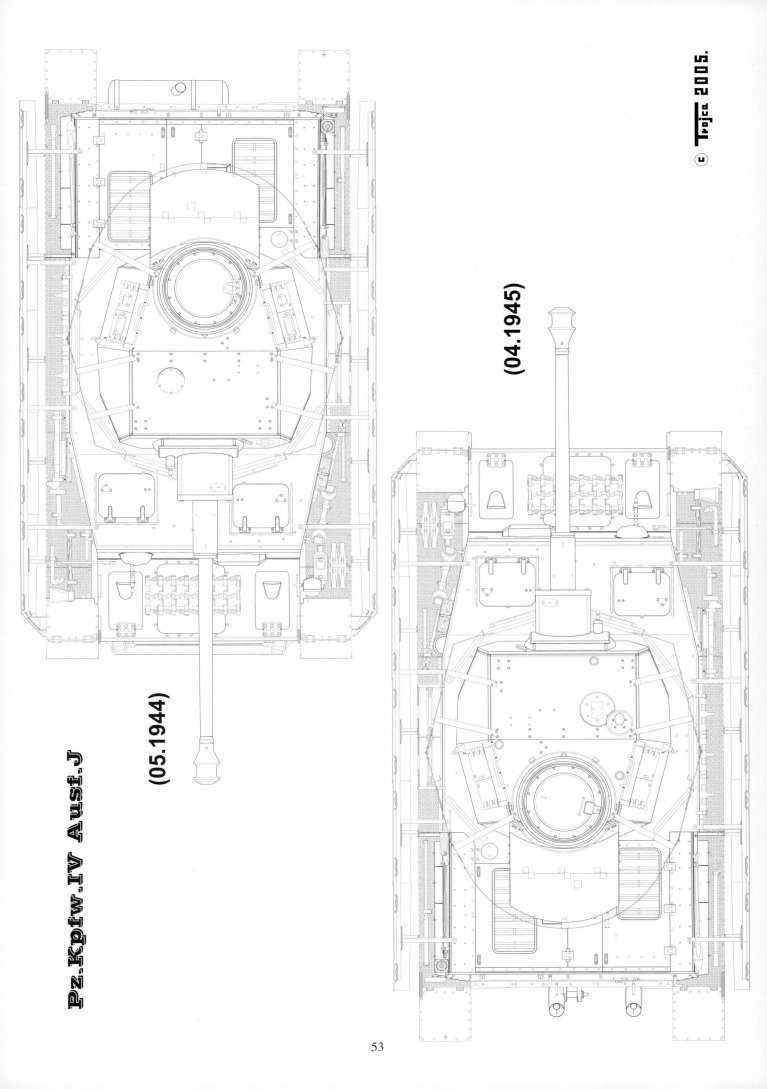

Pz.Kpfw.IV Ausf.J

(05.1944)

(04.1945)

© Trojca 2005.

53

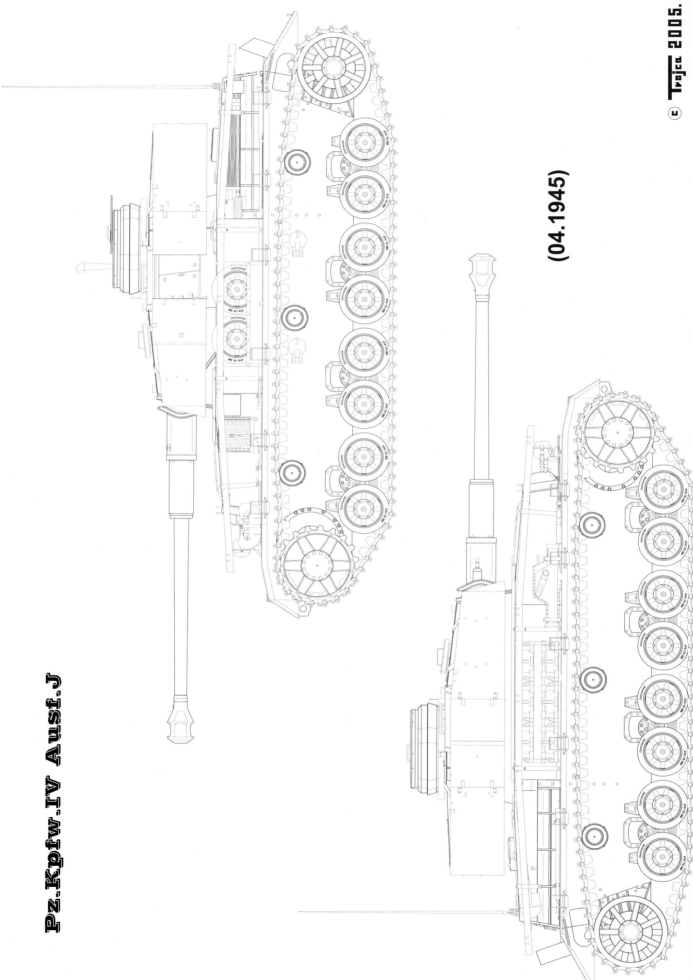

Pz.Kpfw.IV Ausf.J

(04.1945)

© Trojca 2005.

54

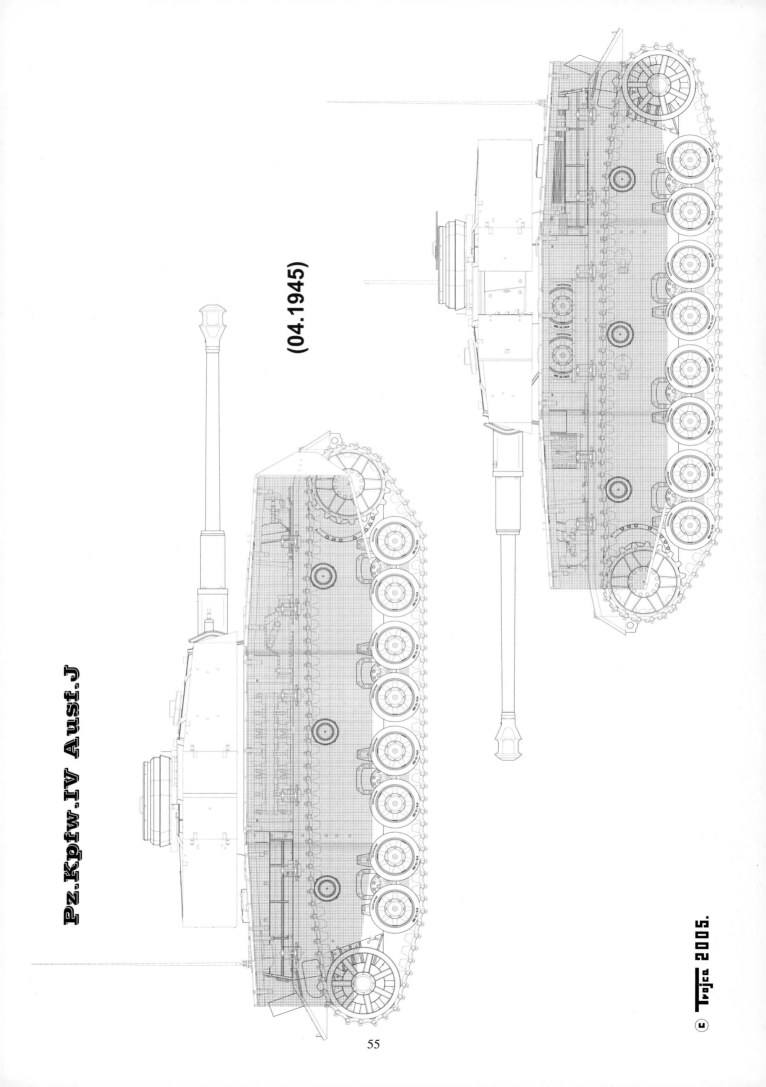

Pz.Kpfw.IV Ausf.J

(04.1945)

© Trojca 2005.

55

(04.1945)

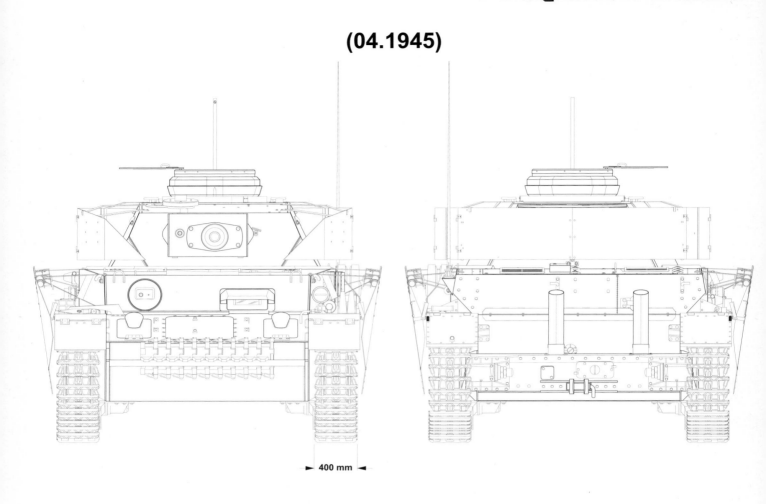

400 mm

(12.1944)

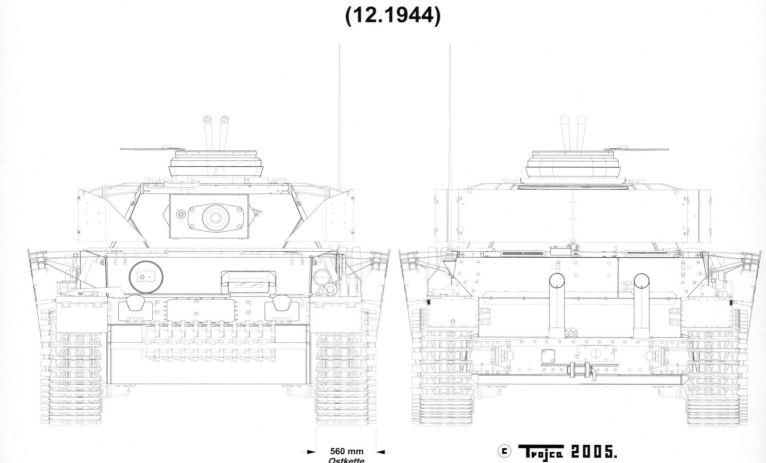

560 mm
Ostkette

© Trojca 2005.

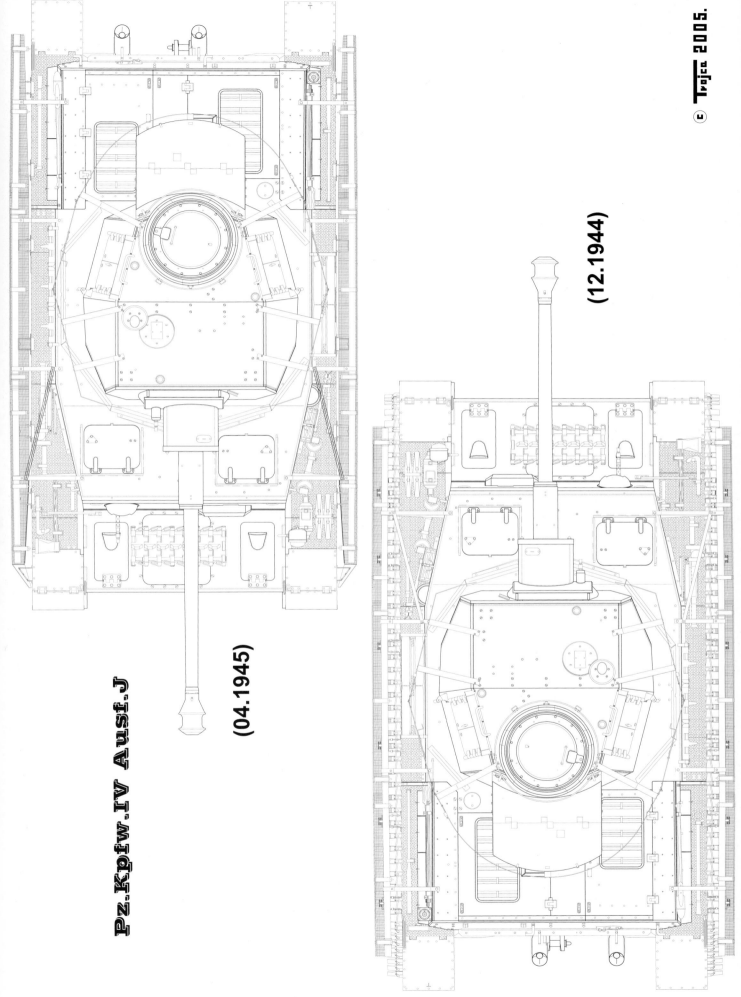

Pz.Kpfw.IV Ausf.J

(04.1945)

(12.1944)

© Trojca 2005.

Pz.Bef.Wg.IV (Sd.Kfz.267 and Sd.Kfz.268)

The first **Pz.Bef.Wg.IV** was produced in 03.44. The **Panzerbefehlswagen** variants were mostly converted from already built tanks. Only 17 were newly-built in the factories, 8 in 08.44 and 9 more in 09.44. On the outside, the **Pz.Bef.Wg.IV** differed from the standard **Pz.Kpfw.IV Auf.G, H** and **J's** only in the number of antennas. Due to the difference in equipment, there were two variants; the **Sd.Kfz.267** (equipped with the **Fu 5** and **Fu 8** radios) cooperated with other armor formations, and the **Sd.Kfz.268** (equipped with the **Fu 5** and **Fu 7**), nicknamed the **Flivo**, cooperated with the Luftwaffe. In the **Pz.Bef.Wg.IV**, the following equipment (which was present in the **Pz.Kpfw.IV Ausf.G, H** and **J** variants) was deleted; the turret MG 34, along with its mount, firing mechanism and toolbox. The number of rounds for the main gun was reduced from 87 to 15 and the machinegun ammunition was reduced from 21 belts (150 rounds in each) to 16. The **Pz.Bef.Wg.IV** had the following equipment added; **Bordsprechanlage B** for the **Pz.Bef.Wg.**, an **Fu 5** radio in the turret, an **Fu 8** or **Fu 7** radio built in between the radio operator's and driver's stations, a container with spare parts for the radios, a **Stabantenne D** antenna (for the **Fu 8**) with cable, a **1.4 m Stabantenne** (for the **Fu 7**), and a **Stabantenne 2** antenna (for the **Fu 5**). An additional **GG 400/12** generator (600 watts) was carried inside the hull on the left side of the fighting compartment (by the wall which separated it from the engine compartment). It was powered by a gasoline motor (.9 hp). On the exterior right side of the rear wall of the engine compartment was constructed a **Panzertopf** armored housing for the base and the **Antennendurchführung 16** linking cable for the **Sternantenne D**. The **GG 400/12** generator was used only when the tank was stationary and its main engine and generator were turned off. Some sources state that this generator was intended to be installed on a permanent basis in the **Pz.Bef.Wg. Tiger Ausf.E** and was supposed to be used inside the tank when it was stationary. In practice, the **GG 400/12** was only used as a portable source of power outside the tank. It was hooked up with cables to the radios inside the tank. Such use of the gasoline powered generator was much safer than operating it inside the fighting compartment. This generator was used in the same manner in the **Pz.Bef.Wg. Panther**, the **Pz.Bef.Wg. Tiger** and the **Pz.Bef.Wg. Tiger Ausf.B**.

The **Pz.Bef.Wg.IV** (and the **Pz.Kpfw.IV Ausf.G, H** and **J**) were equipped with the **Bordsprechverstärker Kst.Pz.Nr.20** (internal communication amplifier) which operated on frequencies 250 – 5000Hz, and which guaranteed excellent voice communications between the individual crew members. The crew had at their disposal the so-called **Schalt-und Auschlusskästen** (switchboards) for plugging in their head sets and throat microphones. From 01.44, the commander of the **Pz.Bef.Wg.IV** was also equipped with the **Schaltkasten Pz.Nr.30 A**. From 01.44, earphones with rubber caps (cap diameter of 102 mm, depth of 27 mm) were used, as well as throat microphones, initially the **Kmk.b** (32 mm diameter) with a three-prong plug, and later the **Kmf.c** with an additional switch on the microphone cable. The **Bordsprechverstärker Kst.Pz.Nr.20** used in the **Pz.Bef.Wg.IV** (**Pz.Kpfw.IV Ausf.G, H, J**) provided for the following internal communication operations:
- The radio operator receives a radio message, and at the same time the commander, the driver and the loader can communicate with each other
- The radio operator and the commander can receive and send a radio message, while the driver and loader can communicate with each other
- The radio operator, commander, driver and loader can each receive and send a radio message
- The radio operator (in the case of two radios) can receive a message on the second radio and at the same time the commander, driver and loader can receive a message on the first radio, and all of them can communicate with each other
- In case of radio silence, all members of the crew can communicate with each other

During combat operations the tanks maintained radio silence (Tn system), and crew members communicated only with each other. The command tanks used a Tg tonlos system for communicating, with a headquarters as an example, which entailed sending encoded messages in Morse code. In both cases, codes were used to deny the enemy the ability to intercept sent and received messages. During operations with infantry, direct communications between the tanks and the infantry was made possible through the use of small portable radios that the infantry possessed. Some of them were:
- **Feldfu. F** (50 channels, frequency spacing every 100 Hz, frequency range 28.0 – 33.0 MHz, communication possible on 11 channels, range up to 2,000m)
- **Torn.Fu d2** (100 channels, frequency spacing every 100 Hz, frequency range 33.8 – 38.0 MHz, communication possible on 21 channels, range up to 4,000m)
- **Kl.Fuspr. d** (21 channels of the radio set divided up from 0 – 100, as well as 18 channels of the 10 W.S.c Fu 5 radio, frequency spacing every 100Hz, frequency range 32.0 – 38.0 MHz, communication possible on 39 channels, range up to 4,000 m)

Due to the shortage of raw materials and workers in the industrial plants, beginning in 07.44, the produced tanks were prepared for possible conversion to the **Pz.Bef.Wg.** If that was desired, the final conversion was completed by the combat unit's workshop in the field. Limited numbers of the **Pz.Bef.Wg.** tanks, however, were still completed directly at production plants. To save materials and time, further simplifications were carried out on the **Pz.Bef.Wg's** in the workshops of the combat units. It was common for the **Fu 8** radio to be located in the turret, while the accompanying **1.8 m Sternantenne D** antenna was installed on the turret roof (this was a simplified mount and, most probably, the 30/80-watt coil normally fitted between the antenna and the radio set was omitted. The simplified **HSK 4218** set also replaced the regular **Bordsprechverstärker Kst. Pz. No 20**. At the beginning of 1945, in the produced Pz.Kpfw.IV Ausf.J tanks the equipment for the **Pz.Bef.Wg.** was simplified even more, and the **Auschlußkästen No 3, 7** and **8**, and the **Kst.Pz.Nr.21 B**, were replaced by the **Kst.Pz.Nr.21 C** and **Kst.Pz.Nr.30 A**. The **Auschlußkästen No 4, 6, 9** and **10**, normally fitted in the hull, were deleted. From February 1945, the smaller **Antennenfuß No 2** antenna mount began to be installed. Already from 07.44, as a cost-cutting measure, instead of tin, the electrical lead heads were covered with a special type of insulating varnish. The crew of a **Pz.Bef.Wg.** was composed of: commander, communications officer (gunner), radio operator 1 (loader), radio operator 2 (bow machine gunner), driver.

Pz.Beob.Wg.IV (Beob.-Beobachtungs)

After definitely deciding to abandon plans to build an observation vehicle (**Beobachtungs-Wagen**) based on the Panther, initially (during the period 02.43 – 04.44), the Germans converted approximately 270 (260?) Pz.Kpfw.III tanks. Later, a number of Pz.Kpfw.IV (mostly Ausf.Js) were also converted to this role. During the period 01.44 – 04.44, a total of 133 **Pz.Beob.Wg.IV's** were produced, of which 112 ended up in the combat units. The **Pz.Beob.Wg.IV**, just like the **Pz.Bef.Wg.IV**, was without some of the interior equipment of the standard **Pz.Kpfw.IV** tank. However, it had additional radio and observation equipment. As its radio equipment, the **Pz.Beob.Wg.IV** had the **FuG 5**, **FuG 8** (mounted as in the **Pz.Bef.Wg.IV**) and the **Feldfu. F** (alternatively, the **Torn.Fu d2** or the **Kl.Fuspr. d**). As part of the observation equipment, the **Pz.Kpfw.IV** commander's cupola was replaced by a cupola from the **StuG.III** because it offered better observation of the terrain. The replacement cupolas were installed in only a portion of the produced observation tanks. Inside the cupola was installed the **Scherenfernrohre typ 14 Z** (**SF 14 Z**) scissors binoculars, and the **Turm-Sehrohr 1** (**TSR 1**) observation periscope was installed in the turret roof. A compass and a range finder were also part of the equipment of the **Pz.Beob.Wg.IV**. The **Pz.Beob.Wg.IV** was primarily used to coordinate artillery fire in units equipped with the **Wespe** and **Hummel** self-propelled howitzers.

Technical Description of Radio Equipment in the Pz.Bef.Wg.IV and Pz.Beob.Wg.IV

The **Pz.Bef.Wg.IV**, and **Pz.Beob.Wg.IV** (and also the **Pz.Kpfw.IV Ausf.G and H**), was fitted with a **Schleifringübertrager 17 Ausf. B** (a 17-element transmitting slip ring), which closed the electrical circuit between the turret and the hull. It was installed on the top and side surface of the turret traverse mechanism. In case of loss of electrical power to the turret traverse in the Pz.Kpfw.IV Ausf.J, the **Schleifringübertrager 8 Ausf.E** slip ring was used.

The radio equipment (also found as part of the standard equipment of the **Pz.Kpfw.IV Ausf.G, H and J**) included:

Fu 5 – **Funkgerätensatz 5** (Fu 5 SE 10 U) manufactured by the firm of *Telefunken* consisted of: an **Ukw. E. e** (*Ultrakurzwellen-Empfönger e* – an ultra short wave receiver with 7 lamps of the RV 12 P 4000 type), **a 10 W.S.c** (10 *Watt Sender c* – 10 watt transmitter of the c type, 3 RP 12 P 35 lamps and one RP 12 P 4000), the **Umformern Eua** and **U 10 a** (converters enabling direct supply of electrical current from the tank's batteries), **2 m Stabantenne** (StbAt 2 m, a 2,000 mm high stub antenna, equivalent of the 0.18-0.22 wavelength on which the **Fu 5** worked). Its lower part (27 mm in diameter) came with a nut used to attach the mast to the **Antennenfuß** mount (made of rubber and a metal center to which the mast was fixed). Fitted on early vehicles, the **Antennenfuß No 1** had a mounting bolt (24 mm in diameter, 84 mm long) whose rubber part was no more than 104 mm in diameter and 83 mm high and had 6 circumferential rubber ribs. As material shortages became more acute, the **Antennenfuß No 1** was abandoned from February 1945 in favor of the generally smaller **Antennafuß No 2**. This had a 65 mm-long pipe (15 mm in diameter) that functioned as the antenna mount. Its rubber part was max. 70 mm in diameter at the base, 70 mm high and had 4 circumferential rubber rings. Provided with a small ball at the top, the antenna was first manufactured from hard copper sheets and then from steel. The ancillary equipment was: a throat microphone, earphones, a Morse key and electrical wiring. The **Fu 5** operated at a frequency band of 27.2-33.3 MHz and had an approximate range of 6 km. All controls and sockets were located on the front panel of the set. Both the transmitter and the receiver were fitted into identical containers (312 mm long, 197 mm high and 176 mm deep) fixed into a metal frame located between the driver's and the machinegunner/radio operator's positions either on the transmission housing in the standard tank or in the turret of the **Pz.Bef.Wg.IV** near the loader/2nd radio operator's position.

Fu 7 – **Funkgerätensatz 7**, produced by *Lorenz*, consisted of: a **Ukw.E.d1** (*Ultrakurzwellen-Empfänger d1* – an ultra short wave receiver constructed from nine RV 12 P 4000 lamps), a **20 W.S.d** (20 *Watt Sender d* – a 20 W transmitter 'D', five RL 12 T 15 lamps, the **Umformer EUa 3** or **EUa 4** as well as a **U 20a** (converters through which power was supplied for the radio set directly from the tank's batteries), the **1.4 m Stabantenna** (StbAt 1.4 m, a 1400 mm long stub antenna made only of steel metal) and ancillary equipment such as a throat microphone, earphones, a Morse key and electrical wiring. The **Fu 7** operated at a frequency band of 42.1-47.8 MHz. This ground-to-air set enabled radio communication at a range of 50 km with aircraft at a minimum altitude of 500 m. This range dropped to 10 km if a plane was flying lower than 100 m. The range could be enhanced to 13 km through the use of the **Stab-Hochantenne 1.40 d** (StbHAt 1.40 d). In this case the stub antenna was fitted on a tent-like, 4000-mm high extension mast.

Fu 8 – **Funkgerätensatz Fu 8**, by *Telefunken*, included: an **Mw.E.c** (*Mittelwellen-Empfänger c* – a medium wave receiver, nine RV 12 P 2000 lamps), a **30 W.S.a** (30 *Watt Sender a* – a 30 w transmitter 'A' with three RL 12 P 35 lamps, two RV 12 P 2000 lamps and one lamp of the RL 12 T 15 type), the **Umformer Eua** and a **U 30** (converters enabling supply of power from the main batteries), the **1.8-m Sternantenne D** (StAtD 1.8 m, 1290 mm long), partly of the stub type made of steel, fitted at the top with six symmetrical antenna bands (each 10 mm wide and 600 mm long). The outstretched bands formed a diameter of some 880 mm and were first manufactured from hard copper sheet and then from steel. The total length of such an assembly was 1750 mm. The antenna came with a 30/80 Watt coil fitted on the **Antennenfuß** sitting on a porcelain insulator and attached to the vehicle on the so-called Panzertopf mount. Additional equipment included: a throat microphone, earphones, a Morse key and wiring. An auxiliary steel frame was also used to install an **Ukw.E.d1** (*Ultrakurzwellen-Empfänger d1* – an ultra short wave receiver 'D') in place of the **Mw.E.c**. The **Fu 8** operated at a frequency band of 1.12-3.0 MHz and had a range of up to 70 km for the Morse mode. The **Mw.E.c** was housed in a metal container (312 mm long, 200 mm high and 180 mm deep). The receiver weighed 13 kg. The early **Mw.E.c** receivers were fitted with a band filter enabling operation at frequencies from 1534 to 3704 kHz. This was replaced in 1942 (in order to limit production costs of the whole vehicle) with a single filter, which effectively reduced the operational frequency band. The **30 W.S.a** was located in a metal container whose dimensions were: length - 487 mm, height – 252 mm and depth – 234 mm.

In order to enhance the range of the **Fu 8** set when the tank was stationary, the following extension masts were used:

- one 800-mm (700 mm?) long mast mounted on the **Antennenfuß**. This extension mast was fitted with the **Antenennkopf c**, on which the **Sternantenne D** was mounted;
- three extension masts, each 1250 mm long of the *Steckmastrohre (StM)* type, installed on a special mount located near the **Panzertopf**. The **Sternantenne D** fitted to this extension mast was connected with the **Antenennfuß** using a 5000-mm long cable (rubber insulation) that doubled as the antenna in this particular arrangement.

The fall of 1944 saw the introduction of a simplified antenna mast fitted to the **Pz.Bef.Wg.IV** (as well as the **Pz.Bef.Wg. Tiger Ausf.B, the Pz.Bef.Wg**. **Panther** and the **Pz.Bef.Wg. Tiger Ausf.E**). The new extension mast was made of six steel pipes, each 700 mm long, installed in a special mount. A 6000-mm long, rubber-insulated cable, actually functioning as the antenna, was attached to the top of the mast. The whole assembly could also be installed directly on the **Antenennfuß** after the **Sternantenne D** was removed.

The **Fu 7** set was operated with three **Steckmastrohre** extension masts, each 1250 mm long. A rubber-isolated cable connected the top of the mast directly with the radio set.

Pz.Bef.Wg.IV (Sd.Kfz.268), Eastern Front, 1943

Scheme of components of the electrical system in the turm **Pz.Kpfw.IV Ausf.G-J**

Scheme of components of the electrical system in the chassis **Pz.Kpfw.IV Ausf.G-H**

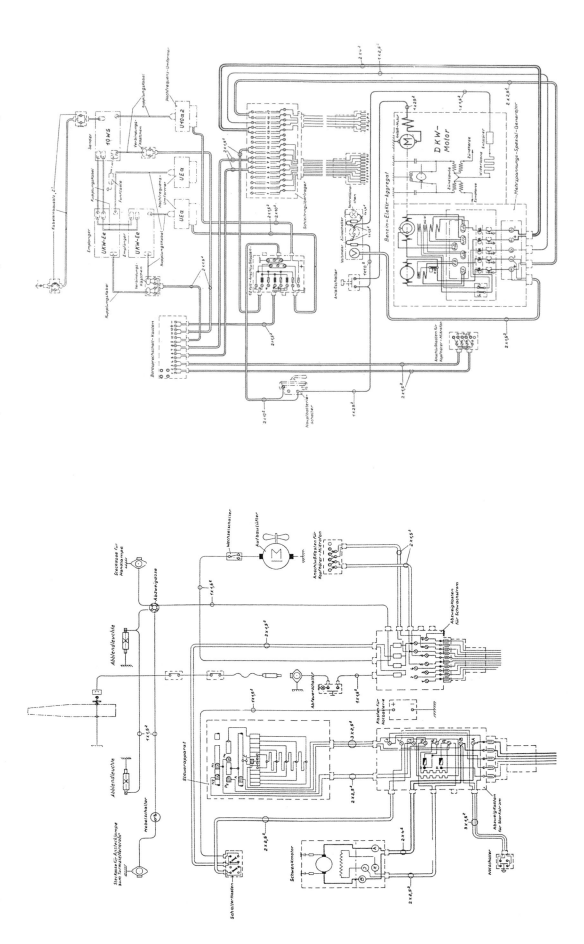

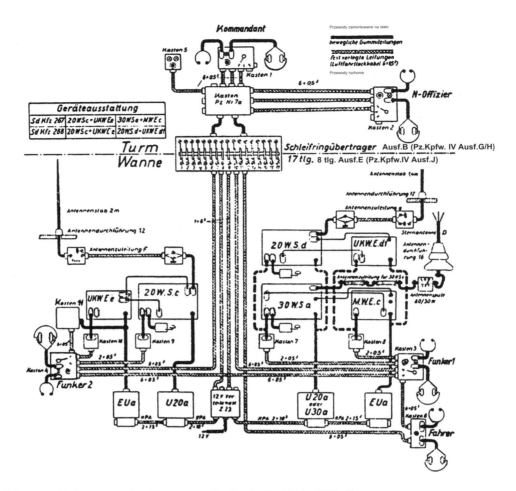

Scheme of intercom and radio communication in the **Pz.Bef.Wg.IV**

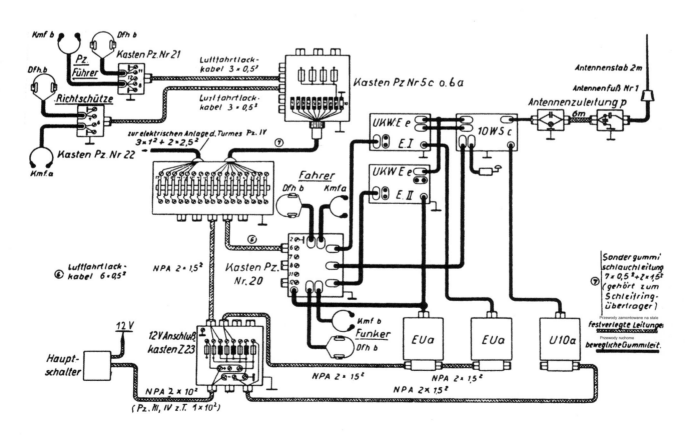

Scheme of intercom and radio communication in the **Pz.Kpfw.IV Ausf.G-J**

Fu 5- receiver Ukw.E.e

Fu 5 – transmitter 10 W.S.c

Two Pz.Kpfw.IV Ausf. G (Pz.Abt.2 of the 20.Pz.Div.) belonging to the 2nd company of the 20th Panzer Division. The tank in the foreground has obviously been converted in the field into a Panzerbefehlswagen. The frame antenna is probably identical to those used on **Pz.Bef.Wg.III**

Pz.Bef.Wg.IV (5./Pz.Rgt.29 of the 12.Pz.Div.), Eastern Front, 06.44, The **Pz.Bef.Wg.IV** (**Sd.Kfz.267**), shown in this photograph, was built on the chassis of the **Pz.Kpfw.IV Ausf.H** version.

Pz.Bef.Wg.IV (II.Abt.SS-Pz.Rgt.12 of the 12.SS-Pz.Div.*Hitlerjugend*), France, 06.44. The **Pz.Bef.Wg.IV**, shown in this photograph, was built on the chassis of the **Pz.Kpfw.IV Ausf.H**. Probably, this is an improvised command tank, as there is only one antenna visible. The **Sternantenne D** antenna has been mounted in the spot where the standard whip antenna for the **Fu 5** was usually placed.

Pz.Kpfw.IV Ausf.J, France, 1944. These carefully camouflaged tanks, photographed during rail transport, are probably of the **Ausf.J** version. The first tank, lower left corner, is equipped with commander's cupola from a **StuG III**, confirming that it is undoubtedly a **Pz.Beob.Wg.IV**.

Pz.Bef.Wg.IV (Kommandeur SS-Stubaf. Jochen Peiper, SS-Pz.Rgt. 1 Leibstandarte SS Adolf Hitler), Ssoolowjewka, Eastern Front, 21.11.43. The **Pz.Bef.Wg.IV** (**Sd.Kfz.268**), shown in this photograph, was built on the chassis of the **Pz.Kpfw.IV Ausf.G**.

Pz.Bef.Wg.IV (Kampfgruppe Peiper, SS-Pz.Rgt. 1), Luxemburg, 12.44. The **Pz.Bef.Wg.IV** (probably) shown in this photograph, was built on the chassis of the **Pz.Kpfw.IV Ausf.J**. However, it is possible that this may be a **Pz.Beob.Wg.IV** (II.Abt.SS-Pz.Art.Rgt.1). Easily seen, are the exhaust pipes with the Flammentöter flame suppressors and the affixed mast extension for the **Sternantenne D** antenna.

Pz.Beob.Wg.IV, Berlin, 05.45.

Pz.Bef.Wg.IV (Pz.Kpfw.IV Ausf.G)
SS-Pz.Rgt.1 LSSAH, 11.43

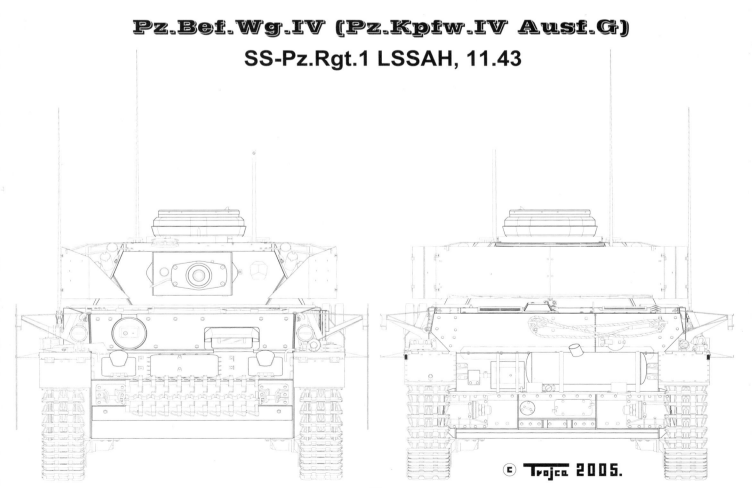

© Trojca 2005.

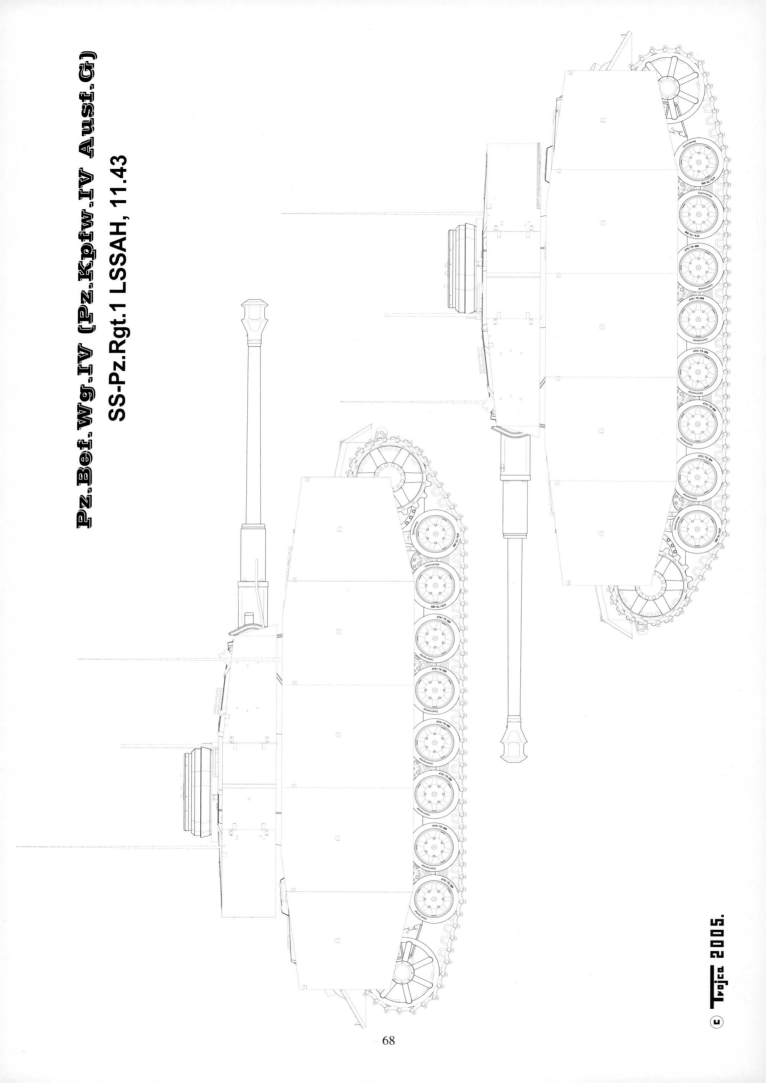

Pz.Bef.Wg.IV (Pz.Kpfw.IV Ausf.G)
SS-Pz.Rgt.1 LSSAH, 11.43

© Trojca 2005.

Pz.Bef.Wg.IV (Pz.Kpfw.IV Ausf.G)
SS-Pz.Rgt.1 LSSAH, 11.43

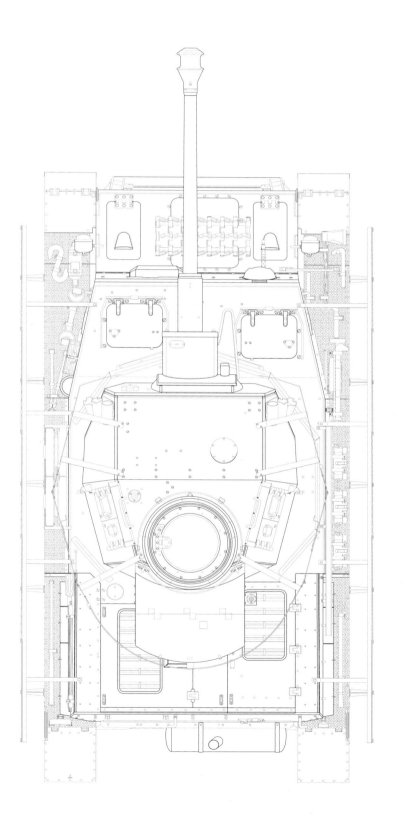

Pz.Bef.Wg.IV (Pz.Kpfw.IV Ausf.G)

Pz.Abt.2 (20.Pz.Div.), 1943

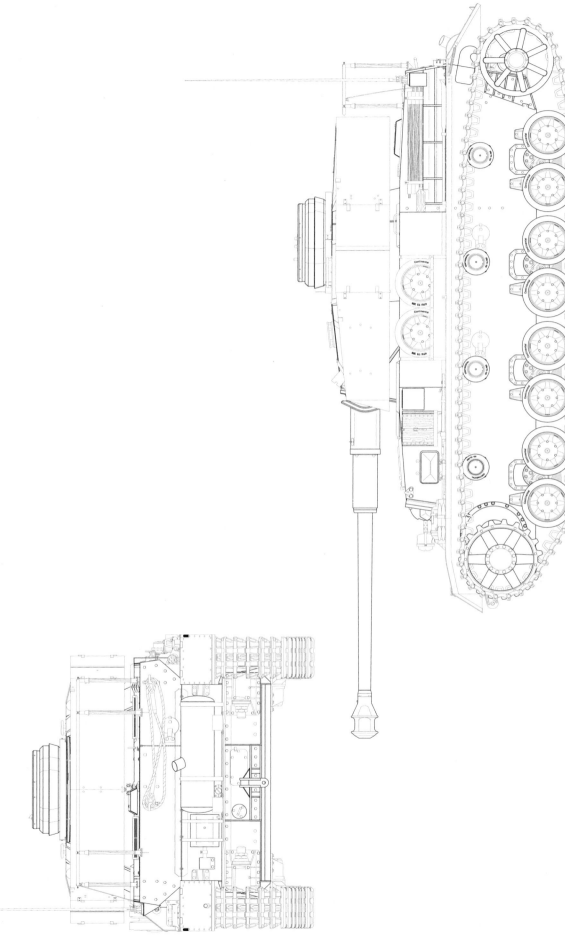

Pz.Bef.Wg.IV (Pz.Kpfw.IV Ausf.G)
Pz.Abt.2 (20.Pz.Div.), 1943

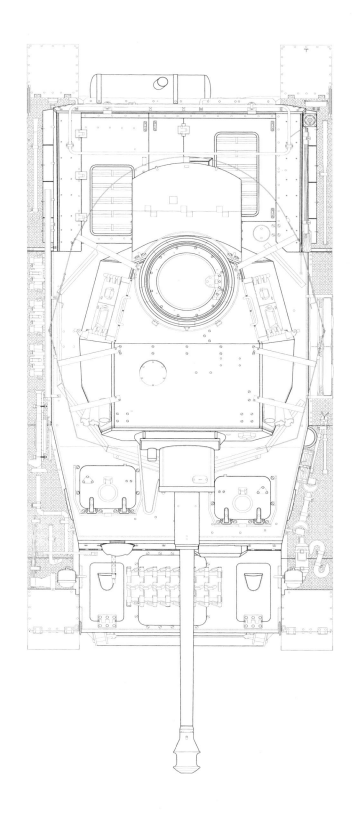

71

Pz.Bef.Wg.IV (Pz.Kpfw.IV Ausf.G)
(05.1943)
Sd.Kfz.267/ Sd.Kfz.268

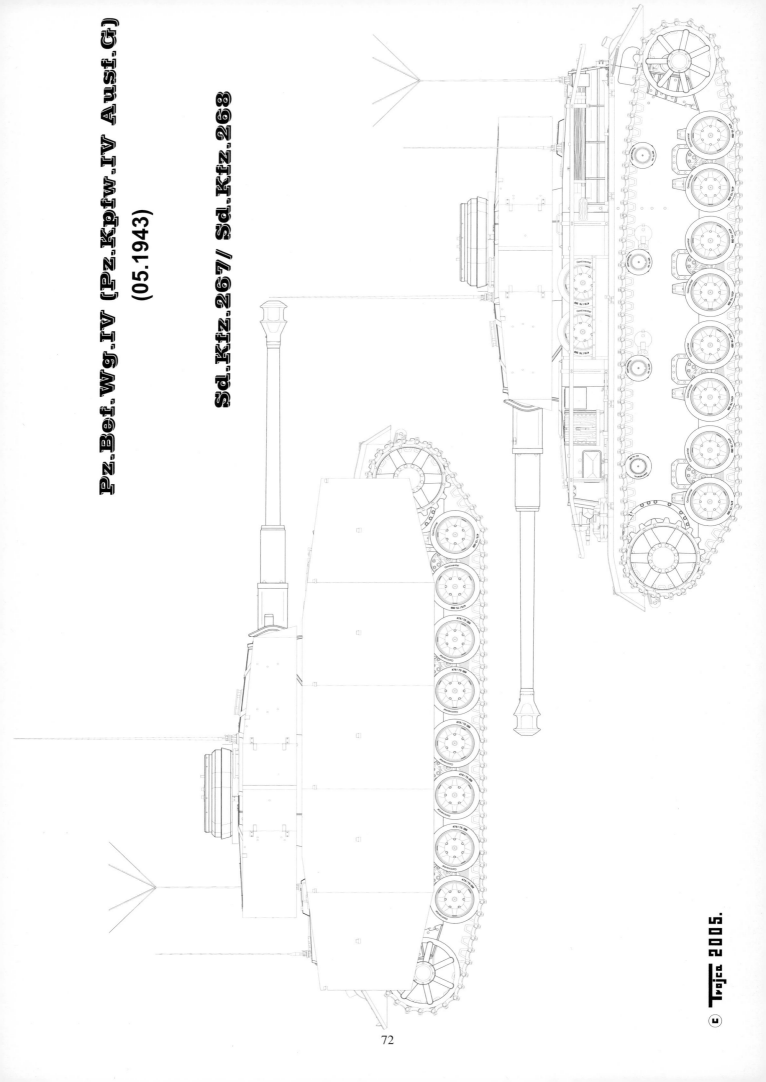

© Trojca 2005.

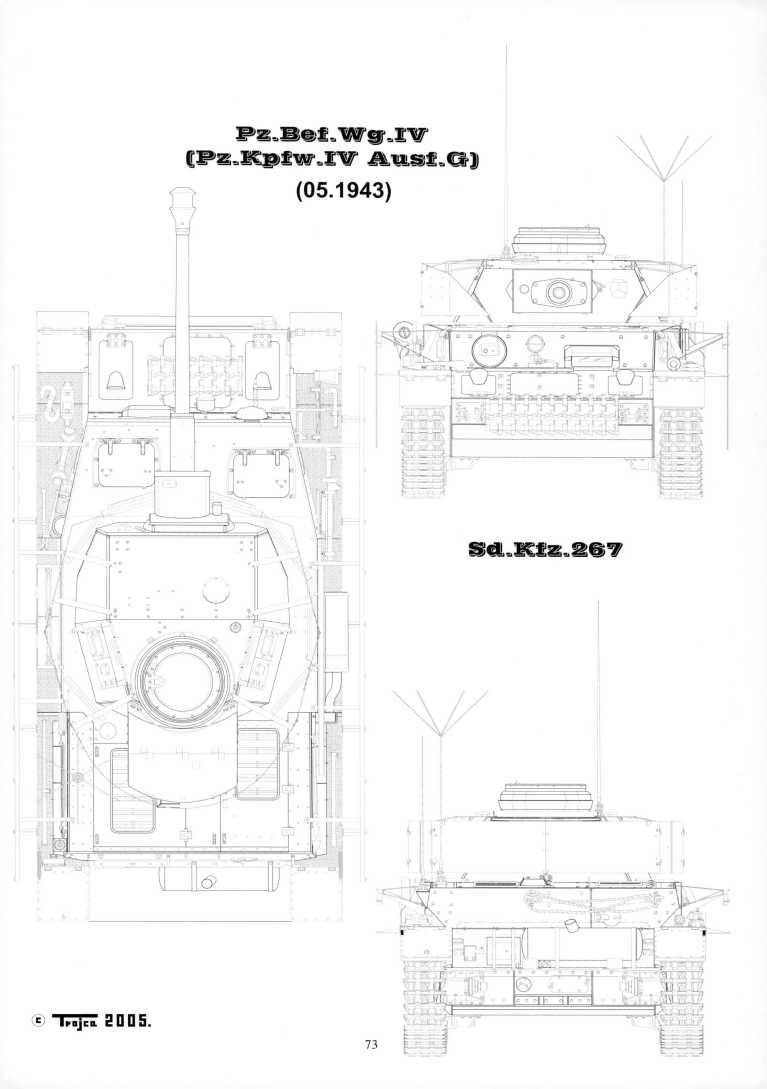

Pz.Bef.Wg.IV
(Pz.Kpfw.IV Ausf.G)
(05.1943)

Sd.Kfz.267

© Trojca 2005.

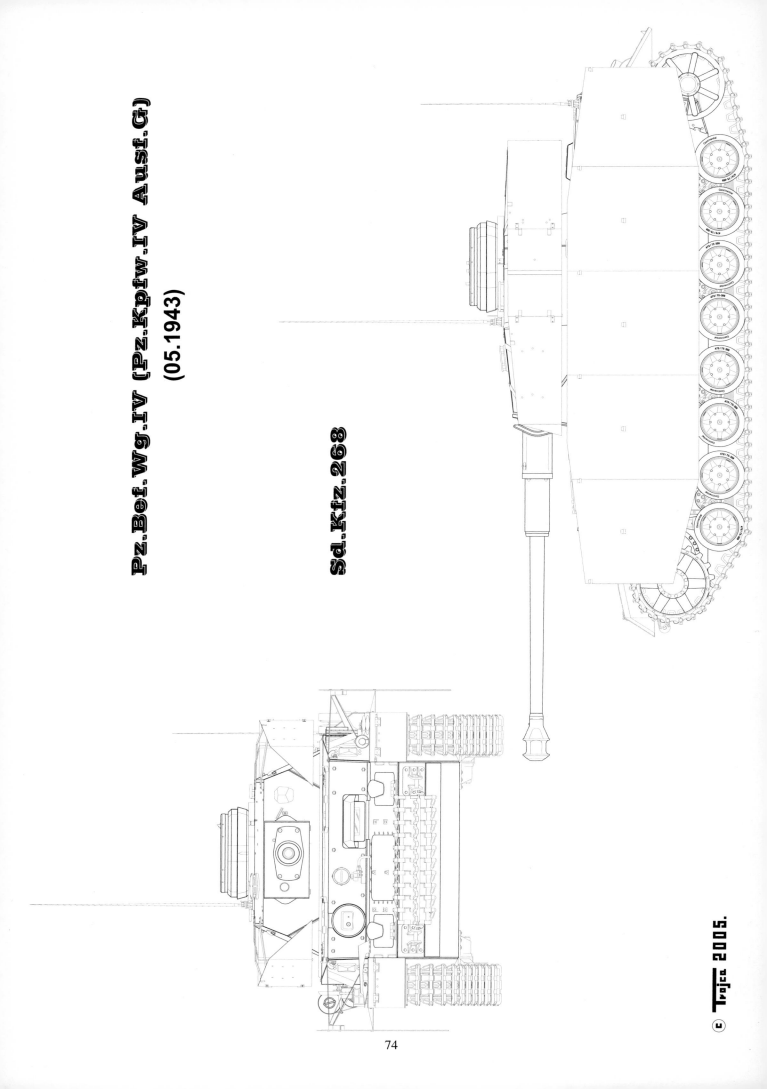

Pz.Bef.Wg.IV (Pz.Kpfw.IV Ausf.G)
(05.1943)

Sd.Kfz.268

© Trojca 2005.

74

Pz.Bef.Wg.IV (Pz.Kpfw.IV Ausf.G)
(05.1943)

Sd.Kfz.267

© Trojca 2005.

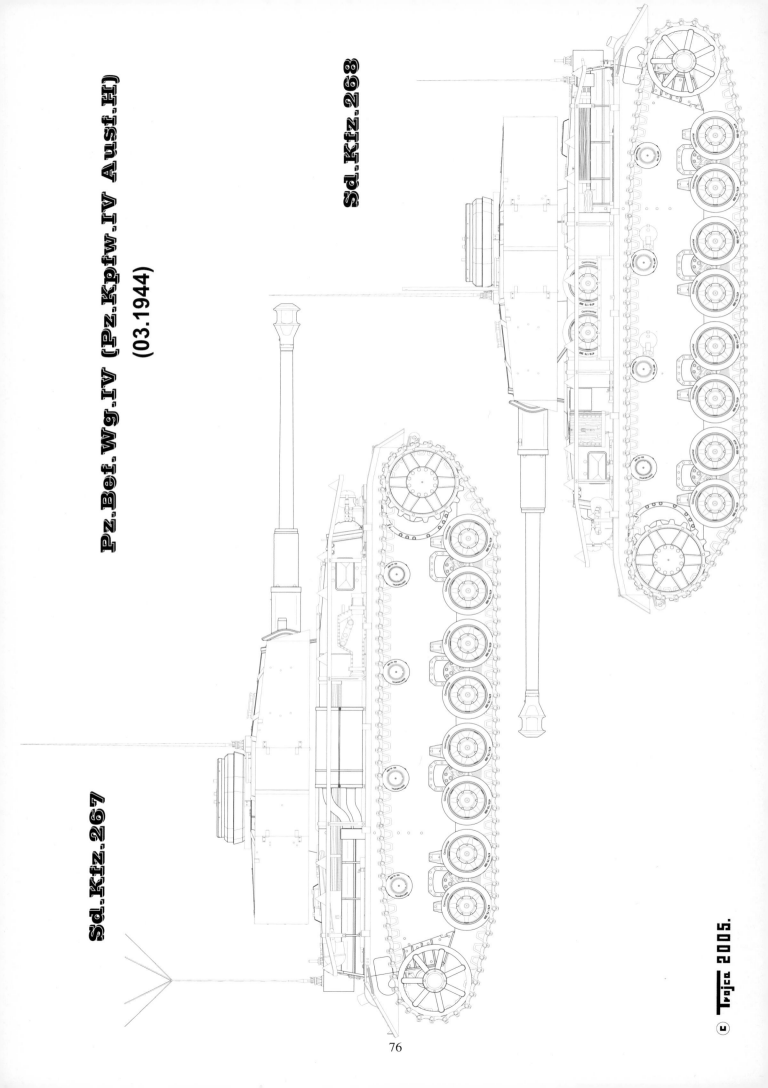

Sd.Kfz.267

Pz.Bef.Wg.IV (Pz.Kpfw.IV Ausf.H)
(03.1944)

Sd.Kfz.268

© Trojca 2005.

76

Pz.Bef.Wg.IV (Pz.Kpfw.IV Ausf.H)

(03.1944)

Sd.Kfz.268

Sd.Kfz.267

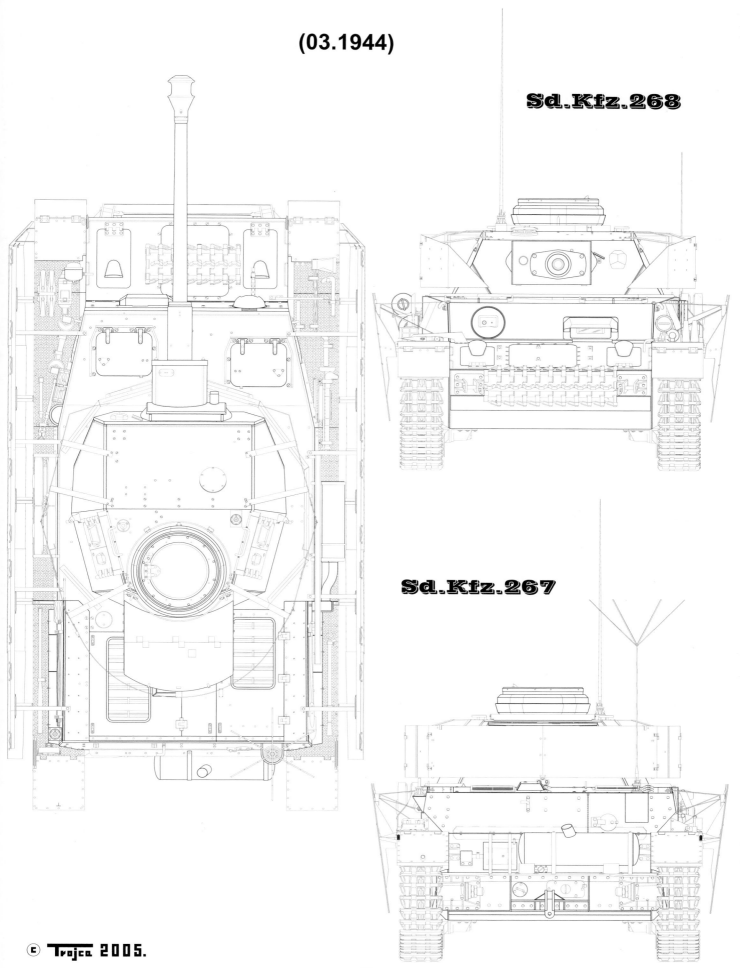

© Trojca 2005.

Sd.Kfz.268
(06.1944)

Sd.Kfz.267
(12.1944)

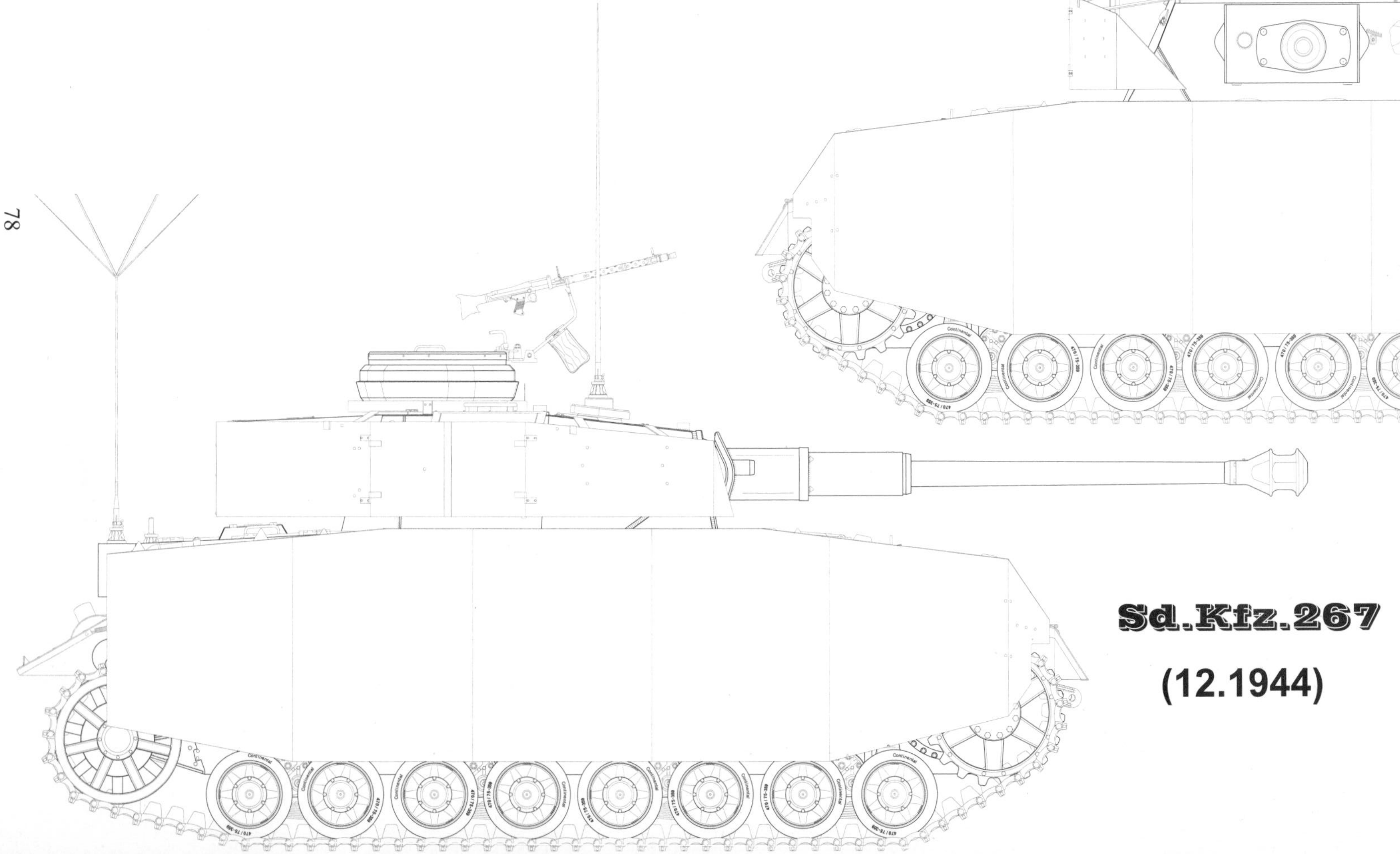

Pz.Bef.Wg.IV (Pz.Kpfw.IV Ausf.H)

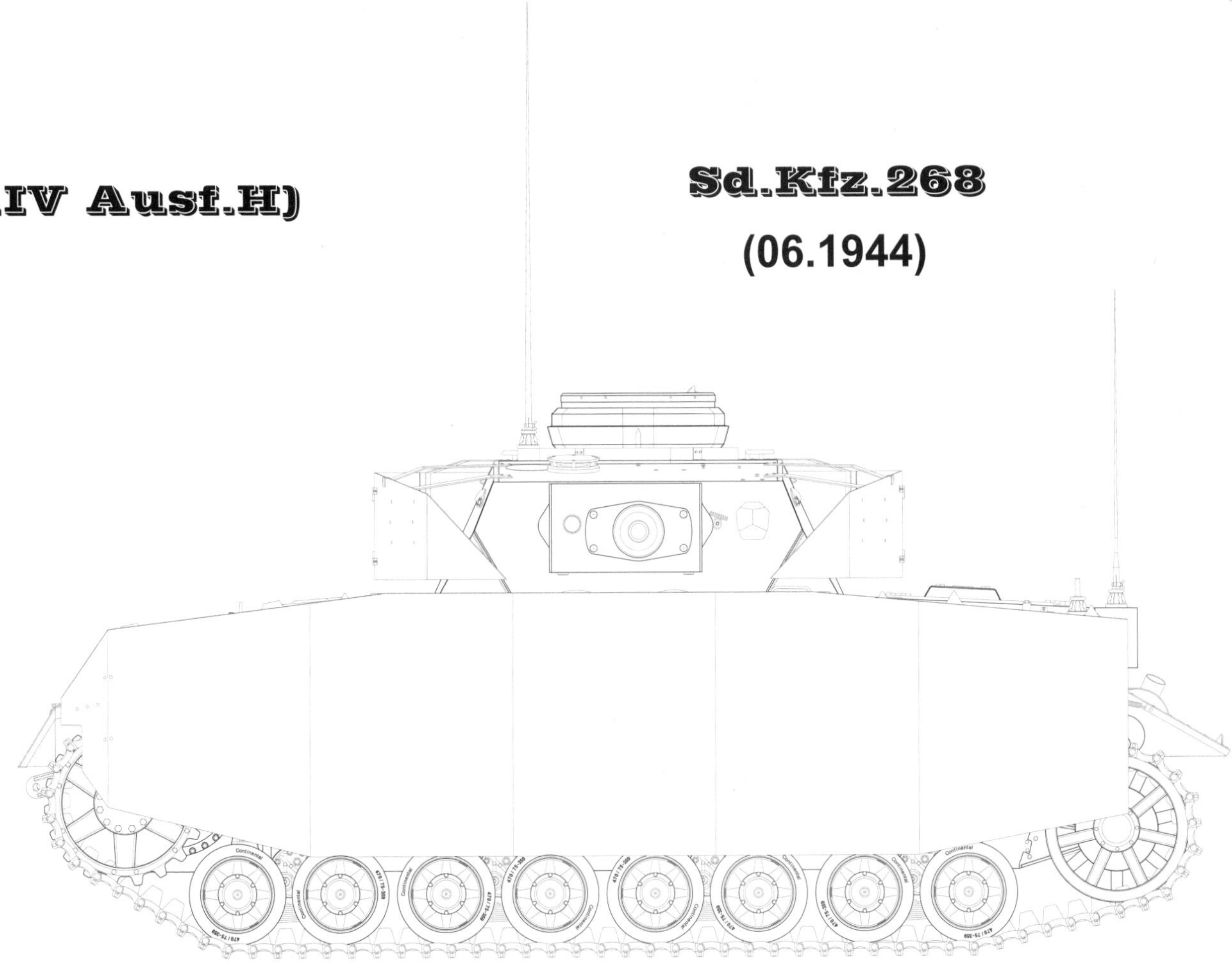

Sd.Kfz.267

Pz.Bef.Wg.IV (Pz.Kpfw.IV Ausf.J)

(12.1944)

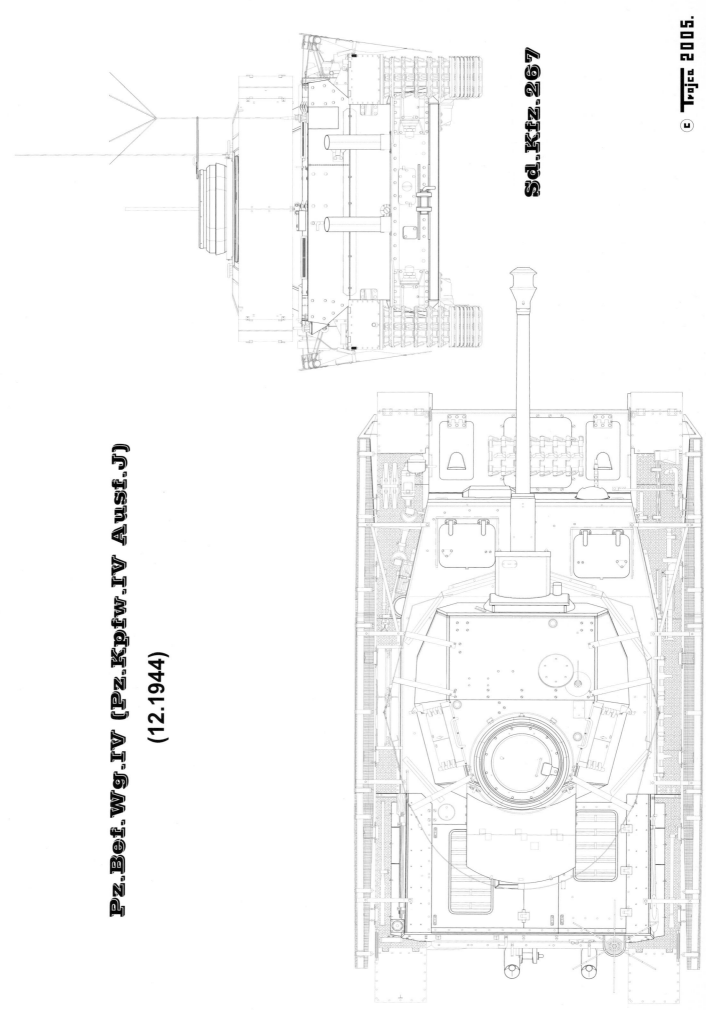

Pz.Bef.Wg.IV (Pz.Kpfw.IV Ausf.J)

(12.1944)

Sd.Kfz.267

© Trojca 2005.

80

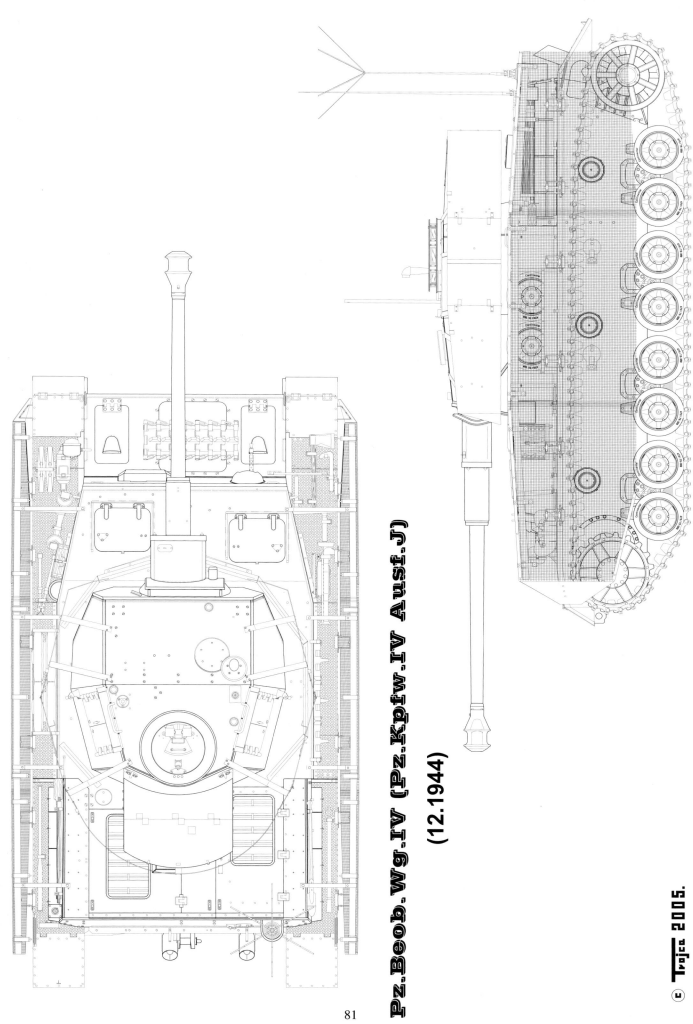

Pz.Beob.Wg.IV (Pz.Kpfw.IV Ausf.J)

(12.1944)

© Trojca 2005.

Pz.Beob.Wg.IV (Pz.Kpfw.IV Ausf.J)

(12.1944)

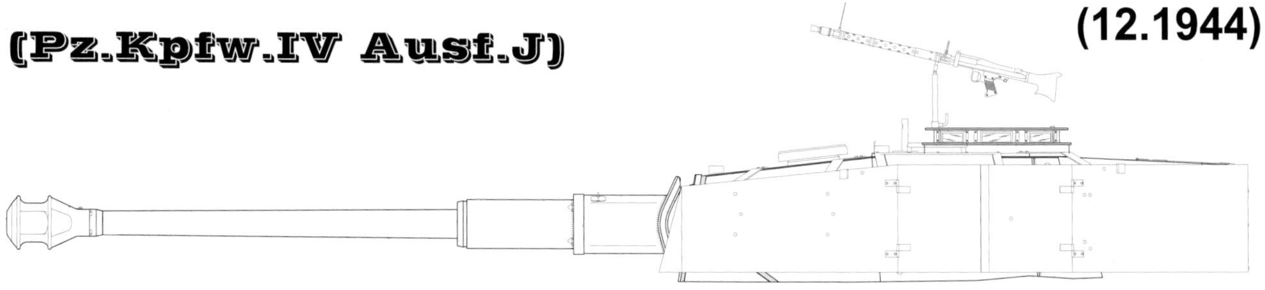

(03.1945)

StuG.III

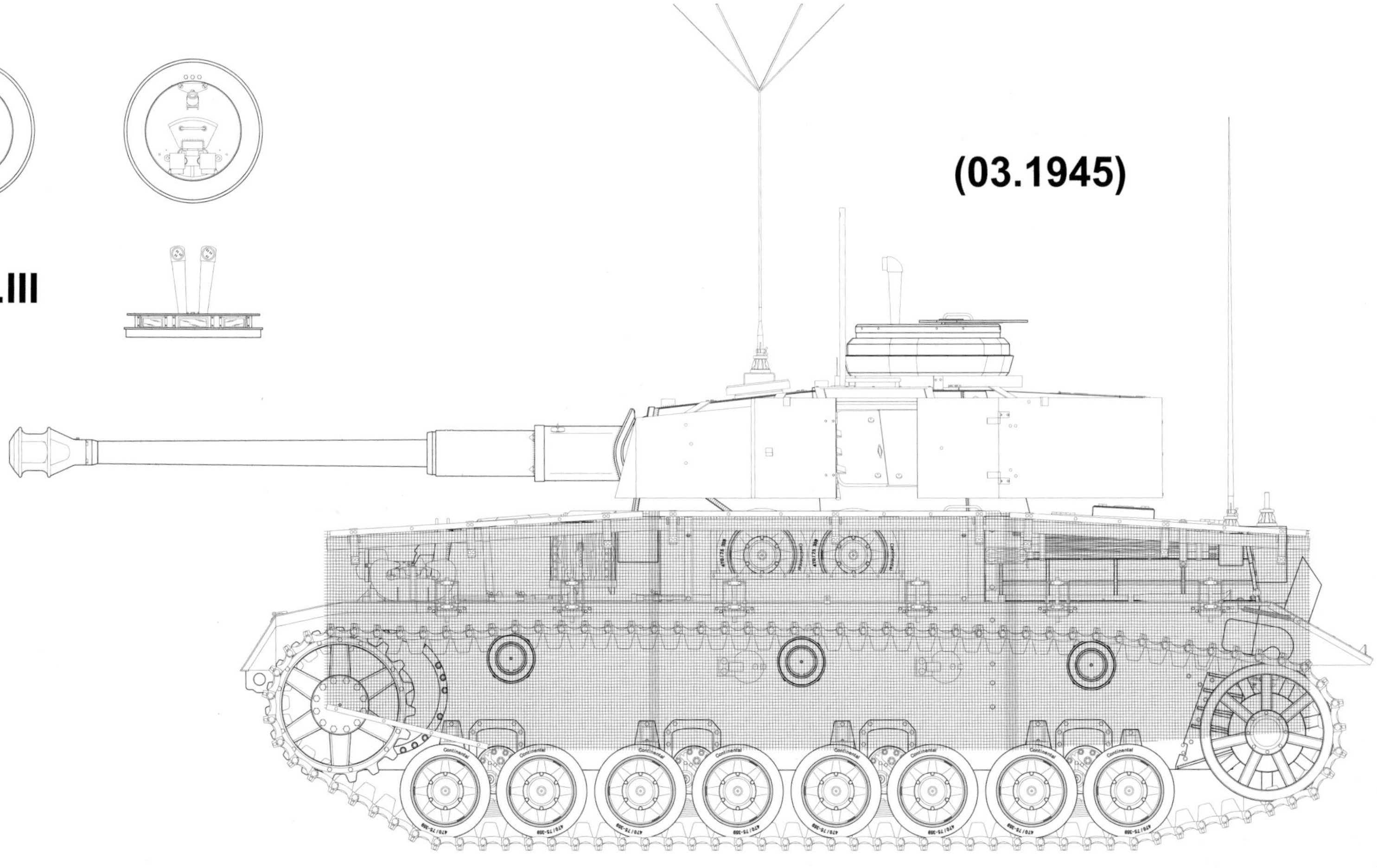

© Trojca 2005.

Pz.Beob.Wg.IV (Pz.Kpfw.IV Ausf.J)

(03.1945)

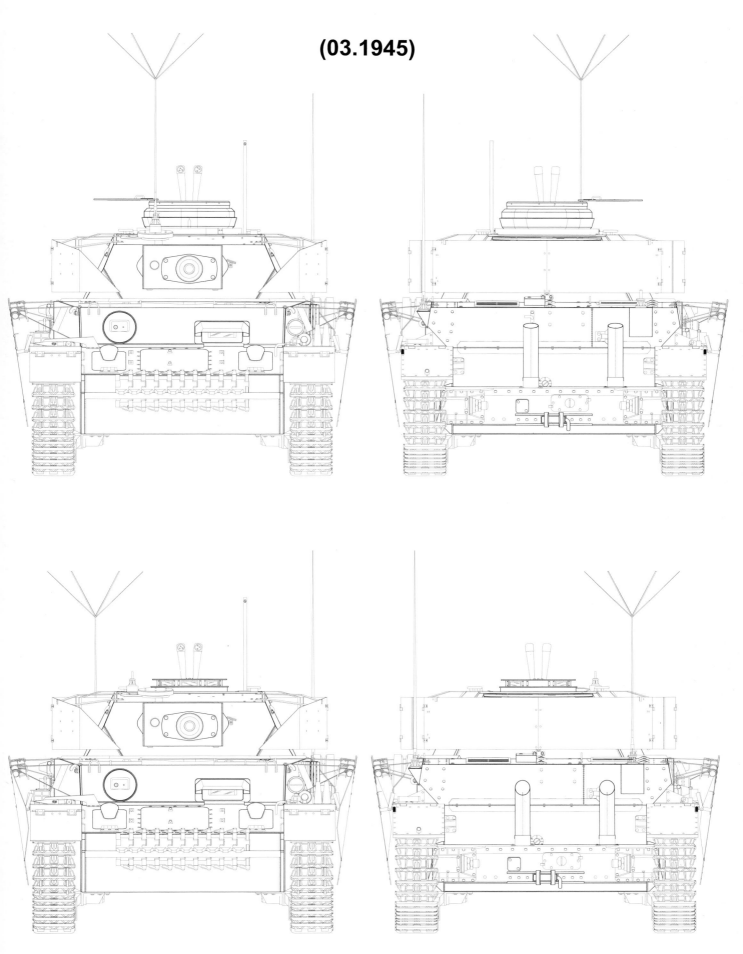

(12.1944)

© Trojca 2005.

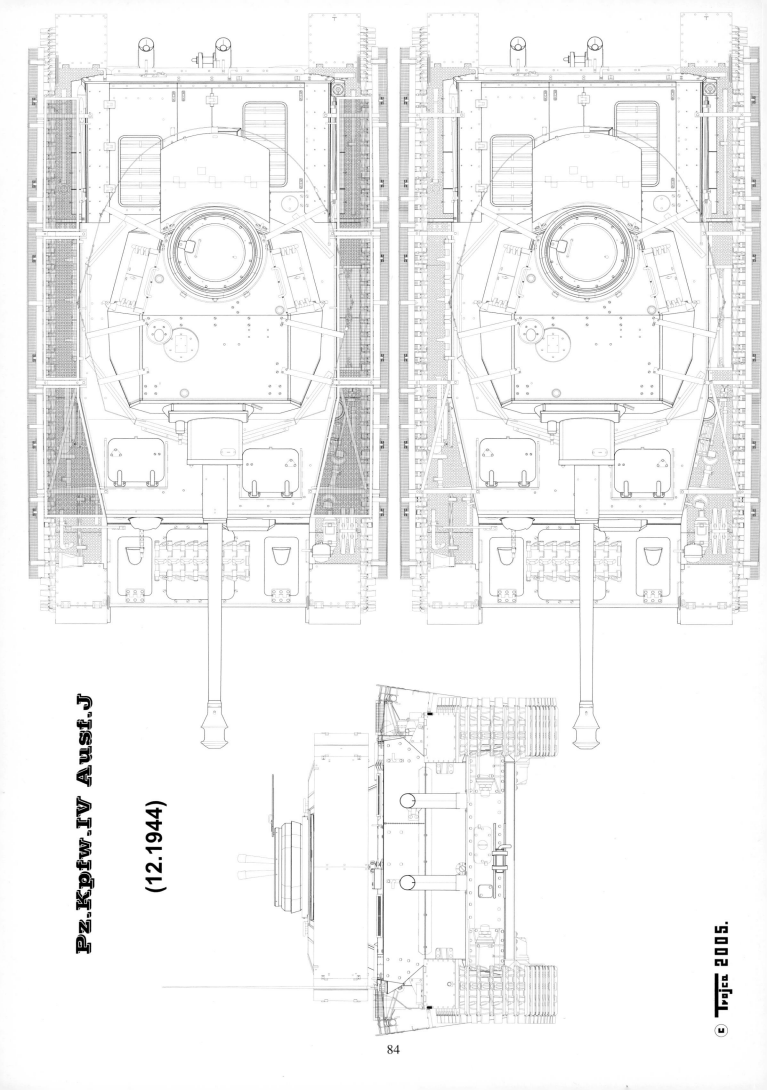

Pz.Kpfw.IV Ausf.J

(12.1944)

© Trojca 2005.

84

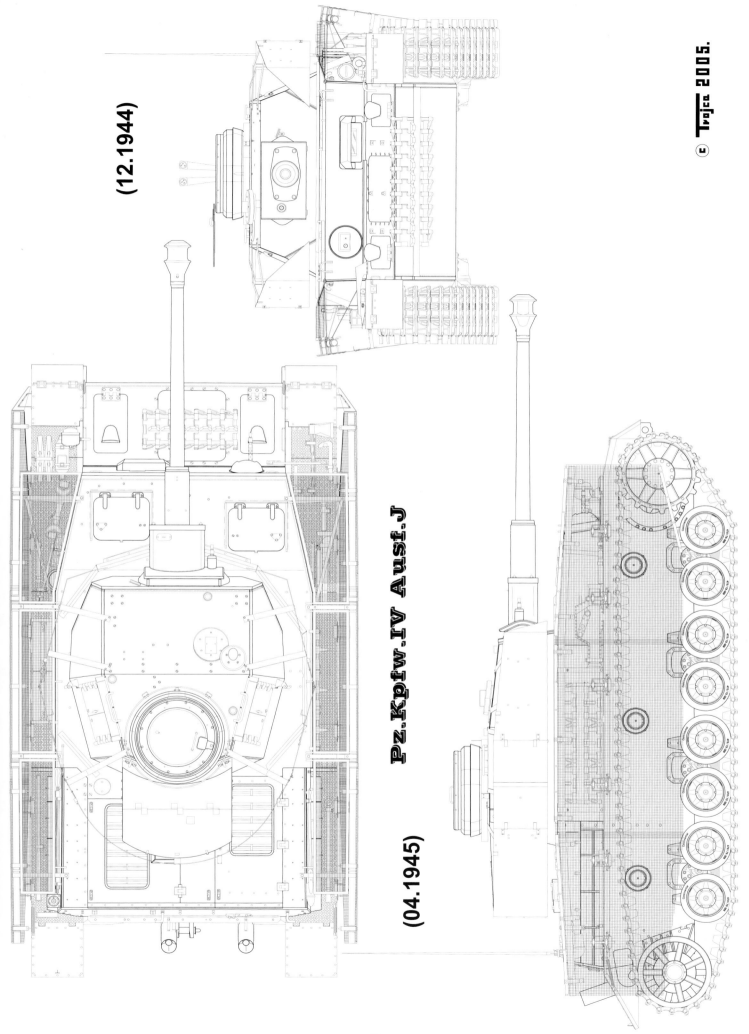

(12.1944)

Pz.Kpfw.IV Ausf.J

(04.1945)

© Trojca 2005.

85

Pz.Kpfw.IV Ausf.J
(04.1945)

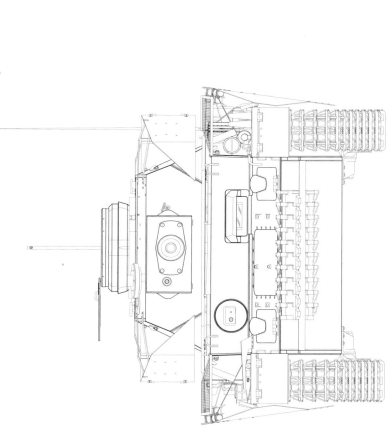

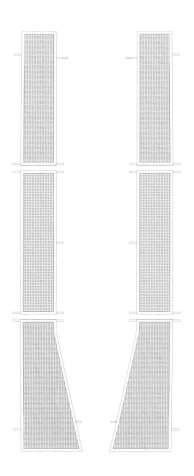

Kompanietrupp

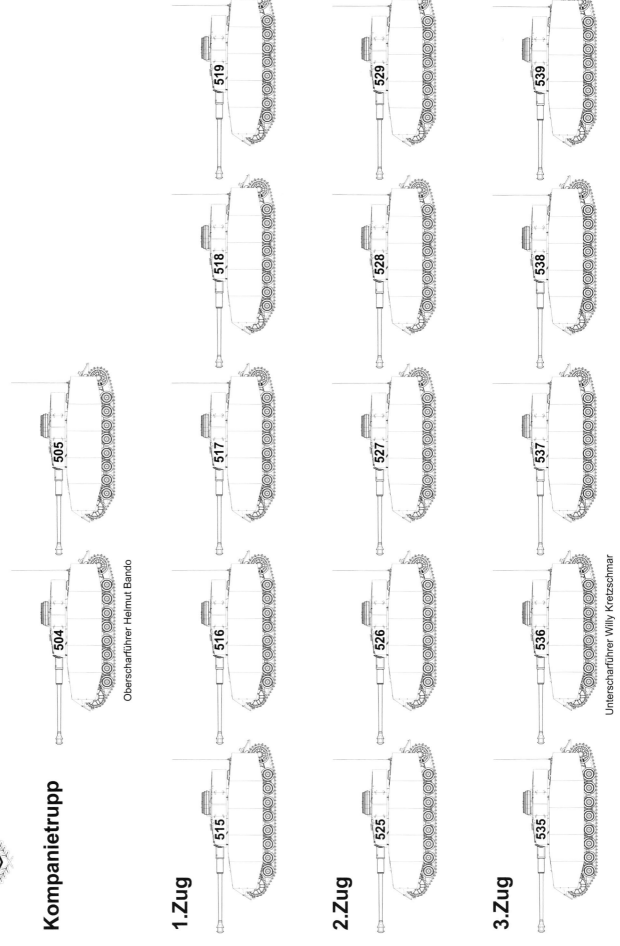

504

Oberscharführer Helmut Bando

505

1.Zug

515   516   517   518   519

2.Zug

525   526   527   528   529

3.Zug

535   536   537   538   539

Unterscharführer Willy Kretzschmar

6./II.Abt.SS-Pz.Rgt.12 (12.SS-Pz.Div. *Hitler-Jugend*) 06.06.1944

© Trojca 2005.

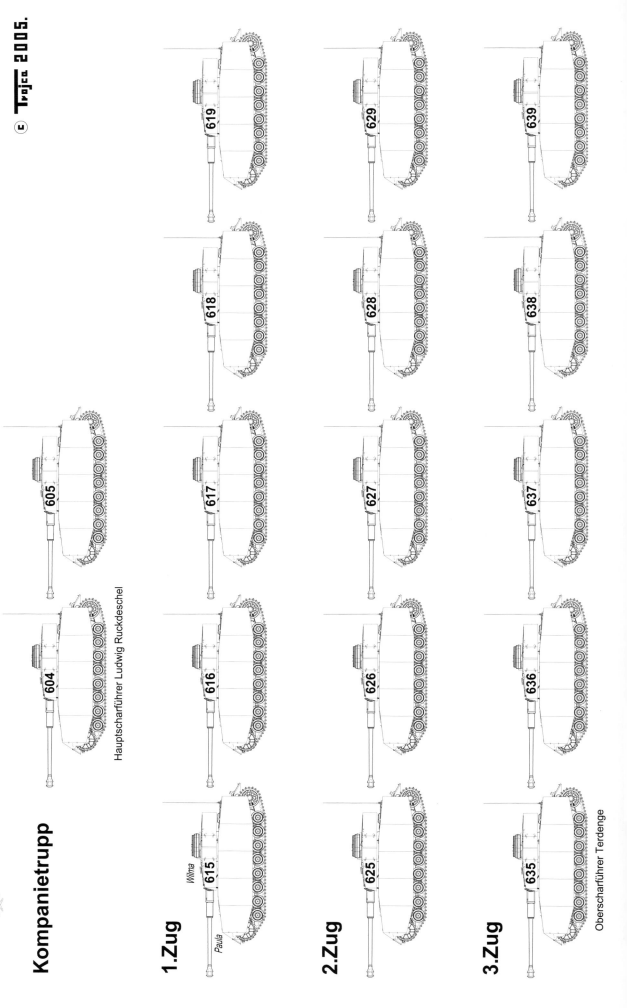

Kompanietrupp

605

604 — Hauptscharführer Ludwig Ruckdeschel

1.Zug

619 618 617

Wilma 615 616

Paula

2.Zug

629 628 627

625 626

3.Zug

639 638 637

635 636 — Oberscharführer Terdenge

88

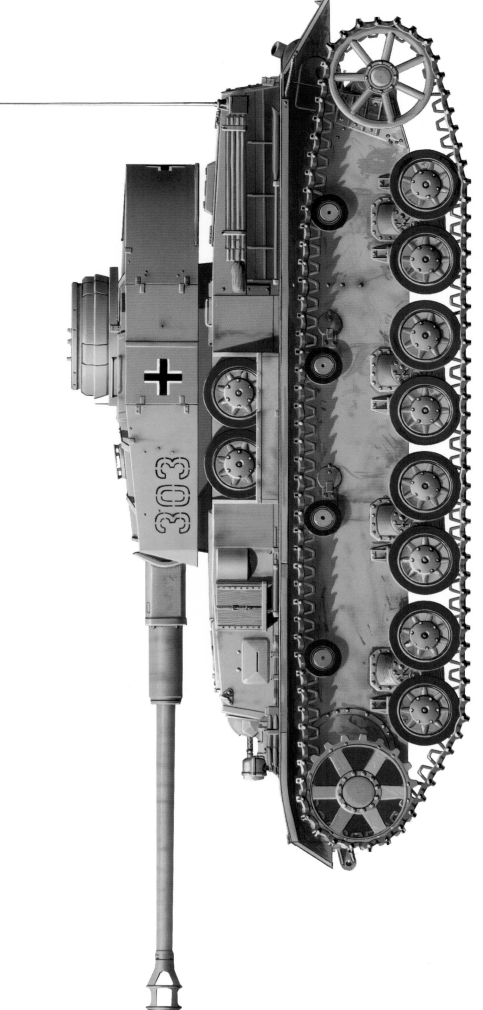

"F 14"

Pz.Kpfw.IV Ausf.H, 16.Pz.Div, Italy, 1943

89

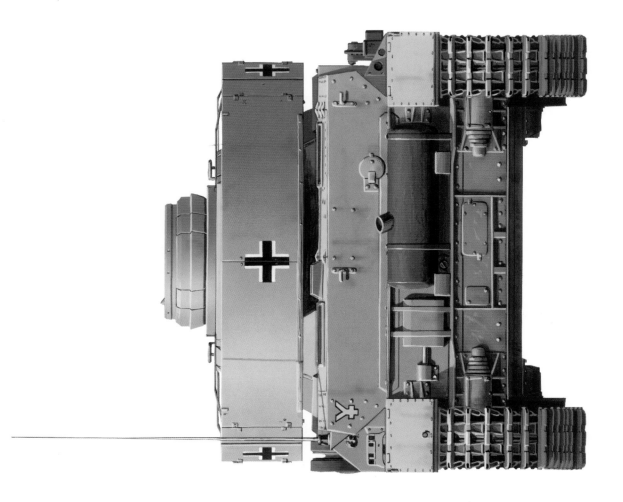

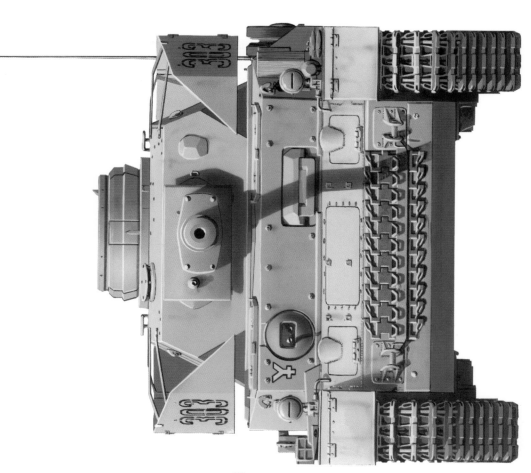

Pz.Kpfw.IV Ausf.H, 16.Pz.Div, Italy, 1943

Pz.Kpfw.IV Ausf.H, 8./Pz.Rgt.3 (2.Pz.Div), Normandy, 06.44

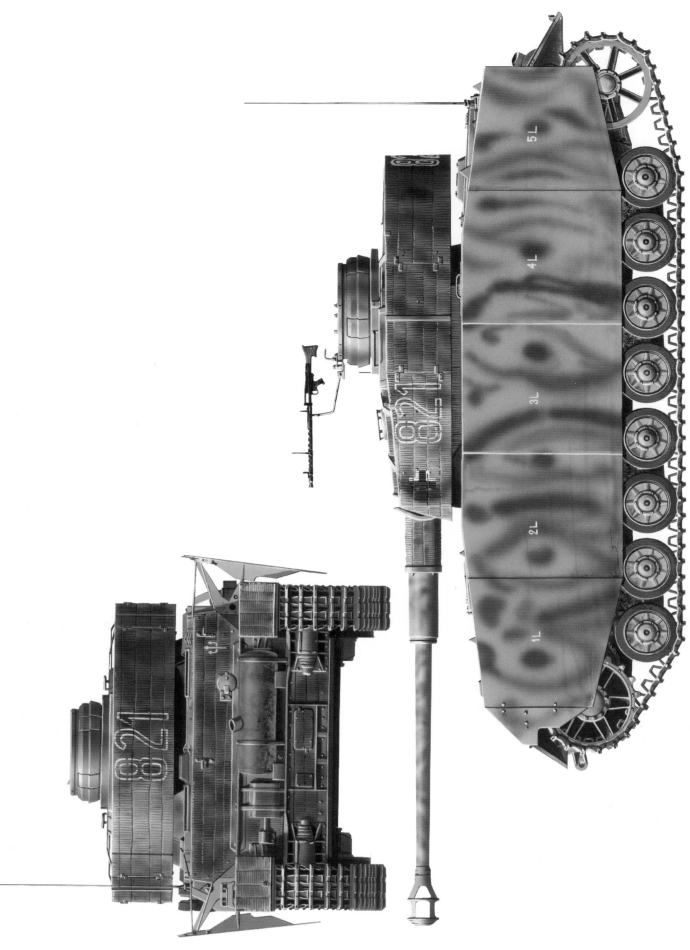

Pz.Kpfw.IV Ausf.H, 8./Pz.Rgt.3 (2.Pz.Div), Normandy, 06.44